Mike Smith is a doctor, writer and broad~~~~~ ~~~~~~
columnist on *Woman's Own*, a reg~~~~~
and LBC's Medical Phone-in Lin~~~~~
problems. He is a specialist in pr~~~~~
Health Service, Chief Medical Office~~~~~
and has been a magistrate and chair~~~~~

Iona Smith qualified as a nurse a~~~~~
became an instructing nurse in fan~~~ ~~~~~~~. This work included
visiting and advising families at home where she saw, first hand, the
problems many mothers face trying to keep their children safe under
difficult conditions. Iona is now a successful journalist. She is married to
Mike and they have a son and two daughters now safely grown up: a
radio presenter, a TV production assistant and a psychologist.

DR MIKE SMITH AND IONA SMITH
WITH MARGARET ROOKE

How to Save
Your Child's Life

The Unique Guide
to Help Children Survive,
24 hours a day

Grafton Books
A Division of HarperCollinsPublishers

Grafton Books
A Division of HarperCollins*Publishers*
77–85 Fulham Palace Road,
Hammersmith, London W6 8JB

Published by GraftonBooks 1991
9 8 7 6 5 4 3 2 1

First published in Great Britain by
Lennard Publishing 1989

A CIP catalogue record for this book
is available from the British Library

ISBN 0-586-21095-4

Printed in Great Britain by
HarperCollinsManufacturing, Glasgow

Set in ITC Garamond

*This book is dedicated to our children
Mark, Claire and Emma in the hope that it will
help them protect their children one day*

Our very special thanks are due to our colleague and friend – journalist Margaret Rooke. It is always a joy to work with a true professional – and Margaret is second to none.

CONTENTS

WHY WE WROTE THIS BOOK

Don't read this book and start to worry.

Don't read it and start to feel guilty. That's not why we wrote it. Read it and feel positive – about how much you're already achieving and how much more you can easily do. By doing it you will be able to enjoy your children so much more.

We have called this book *How to Save Your Child's Life*. That's quite a claim, and of course it's not always possible. But there is so much we can do to protect our children and to teach them about today's world and today's dangers. So much of that doesn't cost a penny, nor is it difficult for you to do – it can be done by communicating with them. We suggest you read the book from start to finish even if your children have already reached the age of 14. Many of the safety precautions and the communication suggestions we give for the smallest children will have relevance for all ages. This book should also interest others who may have charge of children, even for limited periods – nannies, nurses, grandparents, aunts and uncles, friends and neighbours. Anyone left in charge of someone else's child will know the feeling of awesome responsibility that comes with baby sitting, childminding and even helping-out.

What we don't want is for the parents of school-aged or older children to read the first few chapters and think 'Oh no, I didn't do that. I'm a failure'. You may well be being over critical with yourself – it's a common feeling, especially among women. Don't forget, it's never too late to make positive changes. It's never too late to work at truly **communicating** with your child and at making her world as secure as possible.

We've used female terms throughout the book when we are referring to children. Of course unless specified differently, what applies to girls also applies to boys. But as we both work for top women's magazines, *Woman's Own* and *Woman's Weekly*, we felt it would be a good idea to break the mould slightly and use 'she' instead of 'he'. We hope parents who only have sons won't be put off by this.

Having brought up three children ourselves, we've lived through those minutes, days, weeks and years of anxiety, apprehension and downright worry. So we're putting forward a lot of our own experience. We hope and believe that this book will not only diminish these depressing emotions for you, but that it will make those most important child-rearing years both fulfilling and **safe**.

Dr Mike Smith and Iona Smith

Chapter One
FIRST THINGS FIRST

Looking after our children, protecting them from dangers, can feel like a full-time job. And it's a job with a huge array of tools to help us perform it well. There are gates to block the path to staircases, there are child-resistant containers which help keep prying young hands away from dangerous pills and liquids, there's shatterproof glass to keep doors intact even when youngsters charge into them, there are smoke alarms to give us early warning of fire. These are just some of the wide range of appliances which help us carry out our task.

But however well we follow all of the very important guidelines and handy hints for safety inside and outside the home – and we've listed a wide selection of these in this book – we may still only be going part of the way to protecting our children from the many dangers they face in today's world.

We may think that protecting our children is one of our most important responsibilities as parents – but there's another which is equally important and which gets even more important as they get older. And that's helping and teaching our children to keep *themselves* safe. To do this we need to use a tool we haven't listed yet, but which can be spelt out in one word – communication; communicating with our children, explaining life's dangers in a way they will understand, and listening to their thoughts and fears in return. **This is the best safety precaution of all**.

COMMUNICATION

Communication is so important partly because no parent can hope to be perfect – perfect parents do not exist, just as perfect children do not exist. We're all only human. We cannot hope to watch over our children for 24 hours every day, never being distracted by anything else. And it certainly wouldn't help their development if we were with them all the time. In addition, even the most careful, caring parent is capable of making mistakes – of leaving that scalding cup of tea at the table's edge in the rush to answer a ringing phone. Even the most attentive mother or father cannot have their eyes on their offspring for every moment of every day. And even the quietest, shyest, most obedient child can be tempted by what they've been told is forbidden, deadly , or simply bad for them – from the sweeties being offered by a stranger to the cigarette being passed round in the loos at school. We can never be certain that any child, even the golden boy who never has a hair out of place and never forgets his 'pleases' and 'thank yous' won't be tempted from the sensible path.

In short, we won't be with them all the time to make sure they are keeping safe. This means protecting our children is a much bigger, wider, and longer term issue than simply putting all the rules and regulations into practice, making sure our toddler's toys are shatterproof and our own boxes of matches are kept well out of the reach of tiny hands. Of course these precautions are important, but they are not the whole picture. Temptations can get in the way of common sense and anyone can make a mistake.

THE BEST LAID PLANS... A CAUTIONARY TALE

While we were writing this book we sat back and thought about our own children and some of the minor crises that we as a family, just like any other family, went through as they grew up. And here's a cautionary tale which shows that no one is free from those mishaps which occur no matter how careful you try to be and no matter how great the priority you give to your child's safety.

All parents have heard the message, time and time again, that tablets and medicines must be kept away from inquisitive, sweet-toothed children. And if there's one place that rule should be foremost in the minds of the whole family, it's in a household whose heads are a doctor and a nurse who give advice to millions on health and safety and who've seen time and time again, through their work in the National Health Service, the heartbreaking results of that rule being broken. But we have to admit that the Smith household was on occasion as vulnerable to human error as any other..

We were living in a house attached to the GP practice Mike was working with at the time, and of course took the strictest precautions to put drug lockers above the reach of children and lock them securely. One day one of the surgery staff came round and called out to see if anyone was in, but nobody heard her. She left a package on the hall table with a note for Mike. It was a bottle of sleeping tablets for him to deliver to a house-bound patient on his rounds. But within ten minutes the bottle had made its way into other hands. Emma, our younger daughter, then just 20 months old, had found it.

When we found her she was sitting on the hall floor with pills spilt everywhere. Without wasting a moment we counted them. The bottle was labelled 30 pills and we found 29. Luckily Emma had only taken one. It made her seem very drunk and sent her to sleep for ten hours but apart from this, did her no harm. It seems almost too obvious to spell it out, and it still brings a shudder when we think about it, but this incident could easily have been disastrous.

Of course the one who was in no way to blame for any of this was Emma. She was far too young to understand any of the implications of what she was doing, but the reason this story is important is because it shows how easily even the most efficient safety precautions can go awry. It also shows how important it is that we communicate our messages to our children in a way they will appreciate and understand when they are old enough to start to take joint responsibility for their own safety. This is a skill, a very special skill which we hope will be enhanced by your reading of this book. But to a large degree it is a skill you will already have – even if you do not know this and even if you have not fully developed it.

If you have not been able to develop it, it's most likely to be the result of a lack of confidence, a lack of time, or both. Lacking confidence is probably the less obvious of these two and maybe the less easy to identify. But if you're guilty of putting yourself down and feeling inadequate as a parent, never feeling able to relax enough to enjoy the joys of being a mother or father, this is something it's vital for you to fight against and beat.

Iona remembers one mother – let's call her Jean – whom she came into contact with while making home visits when she worked as a family planning adviser in Surrey. Jean answered the ring on the doorbell in tears. In the background three-year-old Gary could be heard screaming at the top of his voice. The harassed mum broke down and told her visitor of the troubles she'd had with her son and the way he never did as he was told. Whenever she told him not to do anything he took it as a challenge to disobey her. Confrontation followed confrontation and it was a battle no one was winning.

Jean's lack of confidence in herself as a mother showed itself in the way she simply couldn't cope with her son. It meant that Gary was ruling her life. When he wanted a fight, there was a fight, and Jean felt too defeated and crushed to break the rules her son had established because that was the way he had learned to fill his days.

Iona started to guide Jean towards a different path – towards giving herself more confidence which allowed her to take control of the situation. Her advice was not to allow confrontation after confrontation, but when Gary refused, for example, to put down a knife he'd found which might hurt him, mum should distract his attention with a better game, say a new and exciting way to build a wall with his bricks. Using this method and others, the atmosphere changed and Jean started to regain her self-esteem and enjoy her little boy, who gradually turned from a challenge into a companion.

That's just one example which shows that good parenthood is down to you and that you should never be afraid of seeking outside help, perhaps from other mothers who may have some answers to guide you or who may just help by virtue of being supportive and 'there' for you. Remember, if you are giving motherhood or fatherhood the priority it deserves, no one will know your child better than you do – and your child, in turn, will know and trust you better than he or she knows or trusts anyone else. You will have a very special relationship and you must have confidence in that and in the knowledge that is unique to you, your partner, and your child. You must use your intuition and your understanding of your child to make sure your relationship grows and matures. If it takes this course, no one will be able to communicate with your child better than you can.

THE TIME FACTOR

But that's only true if you give your children the time they deserve and need. We've already said that having children is an awesome responsibility, and that has to be reflected in the amount of time you spend with them.

It's been said before that no one lies on their death-bed and thinks, 'I wish I'd spent more time in the office'. But it's also true that no one lies on their death-bed thinking, 'I wish I'd cleaned out that teapot' or 'I wish I'd seen that repeat on the telly last night' or 'I wish I'd had that extra pint'. There's no doubt about it – most of our regrets will be about the ones we love, what we've said to them, what we haven't said to them, the time we've spent together ... and the time we haven't.

We can never communicate too much with our children – making sure, of course, that we are communicating on a level they can understand. Even before they can speak they will be receiving messages from you, learning from you. They'll be learning to trust and to love. The lessons they will be learning will not be complicated ones but they will be the basis for their happiness and security in the world.

And when they begin to respond, at first with expressions, laughs and cries, and later with their own words, communication becomes even more important. Yes, there are times you will feel angry, there are times you will feel like screaming, and nobody would blame you for the occasional scream, whether it's a silent one or not. But never forget that your child is dependent on you. The messages you send back to her will have a big effect on her developing mind and personality. The messages she receives early on in life should be 'I care', 'I'm interested', 'I'm listening', 'I love you and want you to tell me what's worrying you'.

If instead she's hearing, 'I haven't got time', 'Not now', 'You're just being silly', she'll find it hard to tell you what's she's thinking as she gets older – and she may not ever really trust the messages she's getting from you. In short, you will not be able to communicate as well.

And if you and your child are going to be a team when it comes to safety throughout her childhood years, those same qualities have got to apply. You must be prepared to give your time. You must both be prepared to communicate.

LEARN TO ADJUST

It's often very hard for parents to come to terms with how quickly their children are growing. Every mother and father of a grown family knows the twinge felt when a daughter first reaches for mum's lipstick to try, and a son's school uniform includes, for the first time, a pair of long trousers. And it doesn't stop there. There's also that rush of concern and pride (coupled with suddenly feeling very old) which you have when they are accompanied by their first boyfriend or girlfriend on their first 'real' date. A whole new batch of worries, questions, fears, are automatically raised. And they are raised for you at a time when your son or daughter will be experiencing a natural desire for independence, along with a possible embarrassment about discussing the new developments in his or her life with you and a need for privacy.

Children seem to be growing up faster all the time. Take, for example, the ever younger ages at which they are taking complete control of whole areas of their lives. Surveys show that until their children reach the age of 4, parents are the sole decision-makers in that constant, crucial, world-wide dilemma which none of us can escape – which toys to buy. By the age of 4 or 5 children are starting to exert an influence and by the age of 8 children are taking the decisions – vitally important decisions to them – all by themselves.

The toy market itself tells us the same story: it is now confined more or less to the 0 to 11 age group. From 11 onwards children lose their interest in toys. Action Man and Barbie are off the agenda, Transformers are discarded and My Little Pony is history! Our 11-year-old's message is clear. In their place on top of the agenda are items which say loudly and unquestionably 'We are growing up'. From personal stereos and cameras to clothes, records, and make-up, we look at their shopping lists and can't help but see our little girls growing into women, our little boys rapidly becoming men.

That's when a whole new set of dangers seems to lurk. We shouldn't delude ourselves into thinking that just because Johnnie is only 11 he's far too young to think of glue sniffing, or just because Jenny is only 14 she's far too young to think about sex – or to be in the company of teenage boys thinking about sex on her behalf.

*We must always try to be aware of the lives our children are really living, not the ones we **think** they are living.*

For us to be aware of the dangers our children may be facing we must learn the signs which might tell us this – from them being victimised by the school bully to swigging back alcoholic drinks. But we must also keep those channels of communication and trust open – and make sure we really know our children, instead of just thinking we do. We must keep our minds open, too. So many accidents have been the result of parents underestimating their children, whether it's the likelihood of their teenagers coming into contact with drug abuse, or whether they've failed to realise that even before babies can walk or crawl they have so often found ways to manoeuvre and roll themselves across a room towards an unguarded fire.

So how do we make sure we know our children and the lives they lead? How can we be certain we are getting our messages through to them and really giving them the attention they deserve? To answer these questions it's important to examine the *way* we communicate and our attitudes towards our children.

THROUGH THE EYES OF A CHILD

One of the most important things we can do is to try to look at the world from where the child is standing, not from where we are. Anyone who's wheelchair-bound will tell you how different the world looks from where they're sitting – well, the same applies to our youngsters and not only from the point of view of how much less they can reach and see. We must ask ourselves what our children might be thinking about a certain situation, what the things we are saying sound like to them.

To any adult it's obvious that when you drop a glass it breaks, when you drop a plastic beaker it's not so likely to. But the child's world is very different from the adult's. Hers is a very logical existence. To your child it may seem illogical that when you drop your lego you just pick it up again, but when you drop an egg it breaks. It might seem so illogical that she may just give it a try to make sure! As they get older your children will always try these experiments themselves, dropping things from bouncing balls to pudding bowls to see what happens to them. It's natural they'll want to try to work out the rules for themselves.

Children take everything that's said to them or that they hear about very literally. We recently heard one story of a 3-year-old called John whose parents were expecting another child. They very sensibly decided to prepare John for the happy event to make sure he wasn't jealous or confused. They gave him a book about a mum and dad in the same circumstances and in it mum gave birth to a little girl called Susan. The new little girl brightened up the lives of everyone in the fictional family.

When the big day came for John's parents, and his mum gave birth, his aunt took him into hospital to see his new baby sister. 'Who's this, John?' she asked, holding up the tiny baby. John thought long and hard. 'I'm not sure...,' he admitted, 'but I think it's Susan!'.

That was a very logical answer from John, and one which shows that even when we think we are explaining things well to our young children and providing answers to their questions, what we are saying may still be slightly too sophisticated for them to grasp. For our older children our mistake might be the opposite one – we may be underestimating and patronising them.

TRUE COMMUNICATION

So as well as outlining why we believe communication is an important key to a safe home, we think we need to explain what we mean by true communication. For it's only true communication which will enable you to get your message across and which will allow you to know your child, her capabilities and characteristics and what sort of dangers she might be likely to encounter.

True communication is about more than talking to your child and hearing what she's saying. It's about listening to her, observing her and keeping a completely open mind about her, the way she thinks and the way she is. So many parents make the mistake of trying to turn their children into what they want them to be, instead of trying to get to know their children for who they are, allowing them to be their own person. That means not making assumptions about what your child means when she says something, but really taking notice. Listening is an art. If you're not listening well you don't know her well.

So if your child comes home from school and says, 'I hate Miss Brown. She's a horrid teacher,' you must ask yourself what the message she wants to put across is, what is she trying to say? Your reaction shouldn't be, 'You mustn't talk like that, she's a perfectly good teacher.' You should respect what the child is saying and ask, 'Oh, did something go wrong for you today? Did you have an argument?' Try to pick up on what she is getting at. Don't interrogate but probe gently, trying to make her expand on what she wants to say without leading her. In this way you will be encouraging her to confide her feelings and you will be listening with great care to what she is saying.

In the same way, some parents will deny that youngsters have feelings of their own; they will try to impose upon their children their own feelings or the feelings they think their children ought to have. So if they see or hear their child being miserable, they might say, 'You've got no reason to be unhappy, let's have a smile.' In other words they will be telling their child what to feel instead of finding out what they're really feeling. It is such a common mistake, when parents are trying to assess their children, that they will bring too much of themselves into the process or will try to make their child squeeze into a blueprint the parents have designed.

It's also important to observe how your child reacts to different situations, from her first day at school to the way she copes with meeting a stranger when you're not in the same room. All these things will help you to know your child, know her personality and know best how to communicate with her about life's dangers without frightening or boring her. These observations will help you to adapt your message to her age and level of understanding, and to her as an individual.

LET YOUR CHILD BE HERSELF

Of course, having said this, it's also important to stress that no parent should swamp and smother their children and over-invest in them. Remember, a child is a small person with rights and interests of her own. You must give her room to be herself and explore herself and her own feelings. And you shouldn't demand that she tells you everything that she's thinking or doing or feel upset if she doesn't. From a surprisingly early age children have parts of their life they want to keep separate from their lives with their parents – they may not want to tell you about all their pals at school or about some of the games they play with their dolls – and providing their little secrets aren't frightening or damaging ones, that's perfectly healthy and normal. They are beginning to make their own way in the world. You don't have to know everything about them and monopolise their attention to understand them.

With the understanding and knowledge that comes from real communication, you can build up a picture of your child's character and feelings and this might help you analyse what dangers they're most likely to confront in life. He or she might be outgoing and adventurous, more likely to be climbing trees than watching 'Blue Peter', or might tend towards a more quiet and sensitive personality – someone who'd rather be sitting and playing quietly indoors than zooming around outside.

A lot of this could coincide with the conditioning which emphasises the division of the sexes. Boys are still more likely to be taught to be active and to be given toys which emphasise speed and strength, while girls are more often presented with dolls and jigsaws rather than cars and toy tanks. Researchers have shown that if little girls are dressed in boys' clothes, men tend to throw them up and down and play more roughly with them rather than coo-cooing and holding them on their knees as they normally would. The reverse is true for boys, who are played with in a much quieter way if clothed in dresses. So boys are often more conditioned to living a rough-and-tumble existence.

Obviously many boys are quieter, many girls are more boisterous. And in any case, not all children fall into these categories. It's also important to remember that there is only ever a limited amount these stereotypes can tell us when it comes to what safety precautions to concentrate on and what safety messages to emphasise. The more active type, for example, may have more opportunity to fall out of a tree and break his arm, but the quieter type would have less practice at tree climbing and might be more vulnerable if one day she was goaded into having a go. A quieter type who is something of a loner and slightly unconfident may feel a temptation to go off with a stranger who offers her sweets, but then a gregarious, very loud, very open child may be very trusting and impetuous and be inclined to accept the offer as well.

So although putting your child into a personality group may help you to prepare her to avoid some of the dangers she may face, it's important not to close your mind to the others which also pose a threat. Every mother who truly communicates with her child can say whether he or she is outgoing or withdrawn, confident or timid, sociable or solitary; some children have a lot of 'get up and go', others will be more thoughtful and cautious. But whatever the case, your child will be a complex character who does not deserve to be pigeon-holed. Just as she is complex, so the safety problems you and she have to confront are complex.

However, her more obvious characteristics might provide you with clues about how best to put your message across. If, for example, you observe that your child continually shrinks from contact with people she doesn't know, she might be telling you, without realising it, that she sees dangers everywhere, in everything she does and in every part of life. She might also be frightened to try a new toy in case she gets her finger stuck in it, she may continually want to be in the same room as mum. If that's the case it would be wise to tone down your message about the dangers of life. It's important to point out where the real threats are and the extent of them, but it's silly to worry her any more. We want our children to lead full, active lives.

GETTING THE MESSAGE RIGHT

One father we've heard of was continually telling his already timid children, 'Don't come near this bonfire or you'll fall into it and burn yourself', 'Don't walk on that sofa or you'll fall off and split your head open', 'Don't climb up that ladder or you'll fall and break your back'. He should have been telling them the safe ways to do those things and the true extent of the danger instead of scaring the wits out of them. As it was those children grew up into timid adults, lacking in confidence, worried about trying new things and not getting the most out of life.

This seems to be a good place to point out that it's important that all parents enjoy their children. To do this and to build up a good relationship with them it's important that you don't spend your whole time being negative and telling them what not to do. Yes, they do have to be warned away from activities which threaten their safety and health, but don't forget to give them plenty of positive messages too. Nine out of ten messages should be positive ones. So as well as saying, 'No, don't run around with that felt pen in your mouth,' it's also important to congratulate your child on drawing a pretty picture and for tidying up her bits of paper nicely. This means your warning message about the pen will stand out as important, but you won't sound like a constant nag. There'll be another message there, too – that you can all have a good time together.

FINDING THE HIDDEN MESSAGES

Another reason which leads us to believe that it's wrong to depend over much on categorising is that it is fairly superficial and doesn't encourage parents to look at why their children are behaving in a particular way. If children take one step too many on a climbing frame, slip and plunge to the ground, we must ask if there are underlying reasons for their behaviour. Are they trying to show independence by taking risks? Are they trying to say, 'I'm a big boy now. Look what I can do'? Or are they trying to wind up mum as they balance more and more precariously on higher and higher levels of the apparatus? They could simply be seeking approval – trying to succeed in bigger and better activities to get attention from you. Similar behaviour can have any number of different messages.

In the same way if a child decides to take sweets from a stranger this could have more than one meaning. Is she meeting the first adult who's ever been really, consistently nice to her, bringing her 'presents'? Is she feeling that she's being properly noticed for the first time? Has she run out of things to do which gain her the attention she wants so badly from people at home, and has she suddenly found herself with another opportunity? If your child has set aside your warnings and lessons and put herself in danger, it is always important to check that you are looking for reasons why she may have wanted to take that risk, other than plain, ordinary inquisitiveness or playfulness. In those cases, maybe it would be more productive for parents to stop trying to change their child and start trying to change the way they are treating their child.

And that doesn't mean one or both parents are intentionally being negligent. If dad continually works late and never arrives home before it's her bedtime, if he goes to business conferences at weekends and sleeps through utter exhaustion during the rare moments he is at home, and if lonely schoolgirl Sally really loves her dad, she might find out the only way to bring him back home early from the office is to have a minor 'accident' and hurt herself. If mum hasn't noticed a few dangers, and accidents have been caused, maybe she should consider whether she is getting too busy and too stressed to cope and needs to talk over how she feels with someone else.

BRIGHT, NOT BAD

Of course in many other cases the behaviour centres on the children themselves. The daughter of a friend of ours was always immaculately behaved and believed her mum instinctively when told what was dangerous and what was not, what she was allowed to play with and what she wasn't. But her son, born two years later, couldn't have been more different. If she told him not to touch the electric fire because it would hurt him, he would go and touch it. Lots of screaming and crying would follow but then he'd go and touch it again, just to make sure. 'Janet' always assumed he wasn't very bright and this was the reason he always misbehaved. She later found out he was, in fact, exceptionally bright, exceptionally inquisitive and inquiring and his behaviour was simply the result of wanting to find things out for himself.

This wasn't something she could have been expected to know instinctively about her child, but it is another example of the fact that healthy children don't do daft things in isolation. They are by nature very, very logical. They don't have the huge range of influences we adults have to steer us from our logical paths - from getting drunk to falling in love!

DO YOUR BEST

Janet learned, just as we all learn, that bringing up children is a difficult business. All you can do is try to get the atmosphere right and point out the dangers to them and hope they bring their worries to you. It's often a relief to parents when they find out they don't have to be perfect. After all, the world outside is far from perfect. It's best that they try to be realistic, to have realistic goals, aims and ambitions, to be a good enough parent. No one can protect their children from everything, but we hope this book will enable you to communicate the dangers of everyday living to your children in terms they will understand and remember – to allow them to lead full lives, yet to be aware of all the potential hazards they may face.

One day your child may be alone, walking home from school perhaps, and be approached by a stranger. She will make a split second decision about what to do.

If this happens you will not be there to offer protection and security and to make decisions for your child. You can only hope and pray that your message has come across and your teaching has been worthwhile. True communication, true understanding, and a realistic view of your child as we've already outlined, coupled with understanding the dangers that life presents us with, are the keys to this. They could make the difference between tears of grief – and tears of relief.

Chapter Two
DANGERS FACED BY THE 0-2 YEAR OLD

This book is called 'How To Save Your Child's Life', but of course you can't always do this. Many children die in ways that cannot be prevented, whether they're babies or teenagers. And many parents feel a guilt they do not deserve to feel. They're blaming themselves as part of the grieving process, and it may take years – it may take a lifetime – for others to convince them and for them to convince themselves that they were not to blame. It may be a lesson that they never learn.

But if there's anything that can stem that dreadful self-doubt and self-torture, it must be the knowledge that they as parents did everything they could to protect their children and make their lives as safe, happy, and complete as possible.

All of us have felt at some time or another the complacency of the belief that, 'It couldn't happen to me'. Whether we're thinking about being burgled, getting divorced, discovering breast cancer, being made redundant, it's inevitable that if we're to remain sane we won't spend our lives worrying about the worst things that could possibly take place and whether they're just around the corner. But the most sensible will take steps to try to make sure that calamities are less likely to befall them. Very sensibly they will ask the crime prevention officer round to inspect their homes for weak spots which could attract a thief so they can be rectified. They will seek marriage guidance if they feel their relationship isn't working out. Women will give their breasts monthly checks to ensure there are no strange lumps and bumps where there shouldn't be.

In the same way we should not allow our worries and fears about our children to dominate our lives and detract from the pleasures that unquestionably accompany having a family, but we should take steps to make sure that accidents and disasters will be avoided wherever possible.

And so, from the moment your child is born, it's vital that you begin as you mean to go on when it comes to her safety and health. Preventing accidents, trying to prevent pain and hurt, begins as soon as your new career as a parent begins. The joys of motherhood and fatherhood, especially when compared to the pains of childbirth, can be overwhelming. So it is important not to forget your safety precautions from day one.

A young baby is too young to understand intricate messages about accidents and safety. This book is mainly about outlining possible dangers and how to communicate them to your child and you cannot communicate in that way to the youngest of children. But we've decided that although you cannot *tell* your young baby how to keep safe and out of harm's way, no book on children's safety would be complete without considering the interests of the smallest members of society.

And although this is not a medical book as such, and is more a guide to preventing accidental injury and man-made or self-inflicted hurt and pain than a complete guide to children's health, there are two issues which we feel we must cover which don't come into these categories. The first is cot death, the second is immunisation against disease.

COT DEATH – SUDDEN INFANT DEATH SYNDROME

As a new mum you should already be feeling that huge sense of responsibility that comes with bringing a new life into the world, even if you've had a child or more than one child before. Every baby is different, has different characteristics and patterns of sleeping and eating. Every baby will respond slightly differently, will feel happy or less happy within herself. Every new baby is a whole new experience for her mother and father – and a whole new set of worries about whether she's feeding, looking, growing, behaving, as she should be. And those worries in an overwhelming majority of cases turn out to be groundless.

But while huge sums are spent, quite rightly, on fertility – on investigating conception and the inability to conceive – and while further sums and huge amounts of time are quite rightly spent on antenatal classes, clinics, scans, and new techniques for giving birth, a relatively small amount of cash and time is spent on teaching the new mum about motherhood and guiding her through the first hard months and years. So she will sometimes feel a sense of bewilderment, confusion, and downright fear when she leaves hospital with her precious bundle for the first time. She may have the stark realisation that, in an awful lot of ways, she's on her own.

As she walks from the hospital, she's leaving behind the expert doctors and nurses who only a minute ago were just yards away when she felt she needed them. All that's left, or so it feels, is that tiny armful of total responsibility and total dependency – an incredible amount to cope with when half the time we wonder if we can adequately cope with running our own lives!

Of course, health visitors should be round soon to provide a sympathetic ear and useful advice, so might grandma, and in this day and age both partners should, we hope, be putting the same amount of commitment and enthusiasm into the new arrival, so in that way too, mum should feel less alone. But somehow, to begin with, it never feels quite the same as having your own army of experts and armouries of hi-tech equipment just moments away.

With this background of an acute sense of responsibility and, to start with at least, an almost overwhelming feeling of being left alone to cope with the unknown, it's not surprising that most parents worry about cot death. After all, when it strikes it strikes with a bigger blow than most parents will ever have known before. You've rearranged your life, rearranged your priorities, and then everything you've planned, hoped for and loved so much is devastated.

The reason we wanted to write about cot death, or Sudden Infant Death Syndrome, is because of the extent of the worry it causes. There isn't likely to be a mum or dad who hasn't crept up to their new child's room 'just to check': it's only natural that you'll want to reassure yourself and make sure that all's well. Roughly one baby in every 500 falls victim and that means the chances of it happening to yours are overwhelmingly small. But the worry caused simply by thinking about the possibility affects, of course, far, far more families than cot death itself. This is why we feel it's worthwhile to mention it now – to try to stem some of that worry and to try to help prevent the tragedy where possible.

We hope the figure we've just given may remove some of your

fear. As long as you're giving your baby the priority and time she deserves, as long as you never leave her alone except when she's asleep (and preferably use a baby alarm to check that nothing's wrong if you can't hear what's going on from where you are), there's no point in continually fearing the worst. But to try to make sure the worst doesn't happen, the Foundation for the Study of Infant Deaths, which has spent many years examining the question of cot death and its causes, and which believes there are several contributory factors, rather than just one, has some valuable advice.

The Foundation believes overheating may be a triggering factor in a small number of cot deaths – and there is a tendency by caring parents to do just that by wrapping their baby up that bit too warmly. The rules to follow are to use clothes and bedclothes made from natural fibres. Check if you're using a duvet – it may be too warm. The ideal room temperature is 65 degrees Fahrenheit and investing in a small room thermometer may help keep your mind at rest.

One danger time for overheating isn't in the home at all. It's in the supermarket. If you're both entering a hot store from a chilly street, your baby's likely to be wearing far too many layers for her to be comfortable in the new, raised temperature. Remember to take some of those layers off, even though it means having to stop to put them on again after you're through the check-out. It's worth it for your child's comfort and well-being.

Ninety per cent of sudden infant deaths occur in the 0 to 9 months age group. The high risk time is 2 to 4 months, which is when a baby's breathing can be erratic. And overheating interferes with breathing, which is why these guidelines are so important.

When your baby's ready for a sleep, place her on her side. There is a very slight association between babies sleeping on their fronts and some cot deaths, which could in turn purely be a link between lying on their fronts and overheating. Forget any nativity paintings you may have seen – your baby shouldn't be swaddled or tightly wrapped and restricted in her bedclothes. Her arms and legs should be free and completely movable.

If your baby seems lethargic or doesn't react to you at all, this is a possible danger sign and you should seek medical help. In fact you should ask your doctor's advice if anything is worrying you. Even if you're worried that your fears are trivial and you don't want to waste your doctor's time, it is better to be safe than for your baby to suffer. If you think your baby is ill even if there are no obvious symptoms you should contact your doctor. Never mind if the doctor comes to examine her and says there's nothing to worry about. It is far better to be over-cautious than not to come forward if you fear something's not right. It's far better to do this than to torture yourself for the rest of your life because something did go wrong and you didn't persist in seeking medical help.

You MUST seek medical help urgently if your baby

- Has a fit or convulsion or turns blue or very pale

- Has quick, difficult or grunting breathing

- Finds it exceptionally hard to wake or is unusually drowsy or does not seem to know you.

You should also seek help if your baby

- Has croup or a hoarse cough with noisy breathing

- Cannot breathe freely through her nose

- Cries in an unusual way or for an unusually long period of time

- Seems to be in severe pain

- Refuses feeds repeatedly, especially if she is unusually quiet

- Vomits repeatedly

- Has diarrhoea or frequent loose motions. Vomiting and diarrhoea together can lead to excessive loss of fluid from the body and this may need urgent treatment

- Is unusually hot or cold or floppy.

This is the advice given by the Foundation for the Study of Infant Deaths and we cannot better it. Of course, these are not all signs that a cot death is imminent but they are times when the welfare of your child indicates that professional help must be sought.

It's also important to remember that babies under 4 or 5 months of age shouldn't be taken into great crowds of people because of the germs that will inevitably also be there. The immune system of a child that young will not yet be fully developed. Athough they are provided, at birth, with ready-made antibodies from the mother, these gradually wear out until the child starts to make her own, provoked either by a harmless vaccination or an infection.

Two-thirds of cot deaths occur in the winter months and there is often evidence of a minor respiratory infection which is generally more common in the colder months of the year. Cot death is more common in low-income families but it does affect families in all social circumstances, and boys are slightly more at risk than girls. Mothers who smoke more than twenty cigarettes a day should beware – their babies are at least twice as likely to be victims.

'Cot death' is in fact not a completely accurate description: babies have been known to die in a pram, in their parents' arms or anywhere else.

If that all sounds very depressing, don't feel too much despair. Cot death is not a new problem: unexplained infant death has always been around. It's not even an increasingly large problem – numbers are staying around the same levels. It's only because many other causes of infant death are now being prevented that cot death is the commonest single cause of death of young babies and this is why the issue is given more prominence.

> In fact the chances of your healthy baby growing into a healthy adult have never been so good as they are today. That's the good news. It's very, very good news.

And if you are vigilant and caring with your child and not afraid to seek help when you feel you and she need it those chances will be better still.

VACCINATION AND IMMUNISATION

This brings us on to the other purely medical topic we will be discussing in this book – vaccination and immunisation. We felt that because of its vast importance and because of the misunderstandings that still exist about the subject, we must give advice to parents about protection against disease. For this is the biggest boost there has ever been in the fight against child illness and death.

Having said this, the number of children falling ill and even dying from childhood diseases including measles and mumps is still unacceptably high. And in many regions, the target figure of 90% for immunisation against polio, diphtheria, tetanus, whooping cough, measles, mumps, and rubella (German measles) is not being reached.

It is sometimes thought that certain children should not be immunised against some or all diseases but modern medical opinion says that this is not usually the case. If your child has asthma, eczema or a simple cold, is premature or underweight, is born with jaundice or has a low birth weight, she should still be fit for full immunisation to go ahead – check with your doctor. So is any child with a personal or family history of allergies. So is any child with heart or lung disease, cerebral palsy or Down's syndrome.

Just think – smallpox used to infect three million people a year. Now the virus no longer exists – except in a few test tubes for research purposes. That's because of world-wide vaccination which deprived the virus of its breeding ground and saved so many lives.

Vaccines have also saved thousands of people from other, previously common illnesses, from whooping cough and diphtheria to measles and polio. But the illnesses still exist because high enough numbers are not yet being immunised and so the viruses can continue to infect and so survive.

New-born babies have a natural, passive immunity to many diseases because the antibodies – chemicals produced by the body which destroy germs – are passed on by their mothers while they are in the womb. These protect them for several months. After that they should be protected by the routine, free vaccinations available to babies from 3 months onwards, which will enable them to produce their own antibodies against the specific diseases that are the object of these vaccinations.

Diphtheria and polio are rare in this country now because enough parents are bringing their children for vaccinations to keep the viruses in check. This also helps to protect the tiny percentage of children for whom vaccination is unsuitable. But if the numbers of vaccinated children fell, the diseases could become commonplace again. So it's not only important for your children but for *all*children that we keep the percentage of protected children high.

You may remember a time, only a few years ago, when that did indeed happen with one disease. As a result of serious complications which some people assumed had resulted from children being given the whooping cough vaccine, more than 50% of parents were deciding not to have their babies vaccinated. The results were horrific – major epidemics of whooping cough, a very painful disease for little children, and sometimes a fatal one.

Of course it is tragic if there are appalling side-effects from a vaccination, like the one allegedly associated with the whooping cough vaccine, brain damage. If there are such complications, they are very rare. Yes, your child could be the unlucky one, but even the suggested complications are *six times* more likely to arise from the child contracting the disease than they are for the children who receive the vaccine. Similarly, measles as a disease can cause distressing complications including chest problems, deafness, and convulsions whereas reactions to the vaccine – another one some parents are less inclined to approve of – are usually only slight, if there is any reaction at all.

The new MMR jab, which protects against measles, mumps and rubella, is a breakthrough which should, in our opinion, be welcomed by all parents. Remember, if caught by an expectant mother, rubella can cause deformities in her unborn child, while mumps can cause deafness and meningitis as well as sterility in boys. So many illnesses, so much disease, so much pain – and it can all be beaten if your child is properly vaccinated. With the risk of side-effects being so much smaller than the risk of disease, our advice has to be in favour of full vaccination. Just by making that decision you will be taking a huge step in caring for your children, which will protect them from possible pain and suffering and which could even save their lives.

But there are other threats to your child which need more than that one decision and the occasional trip to your family doctor. They are the threats the rest of this book is about.

For example, did you know:

- On average four children are killed by accidents every day.

- Accidents are the most common cause of death among children aged six months and over.

- Each year one child in every six goes to a hospital Accident and Emergency department.

- One in every three of all patients going to a hospital Accident and Emergency department is a child.

- One in every six children in hospital is there because of an accident.

Most of these facts have been uncovered by the Health Education Authority, whose job includes trying to prevent some of those accidents. Here are some others to mull over:

- The risk of a fatal accident in the home is highest for a child less than 1 year old

- The risk of *any* accident in the home is twice as high for a 1 or 2-year old than it is for an infant of less than 12 months.

We've already outlined the huge responsibility that inevitably comes with starting a family. But these figures show that those we are bringing into the world, those who are the most vulnerable, the least able to protect themselves and the most completely dependent on you, are those most at risk. The latest available figures emphasise this:

Age	Number of accidents in the home
0 - 2	338,000
3 - 4	150,900
5 - 6	88,000
7 - 8	67,600
9 - 10	54,400
11 - 12	48,700
13 -14	49,900

Every parent will know that some mishaps can't be avoided. They can be seen as a part of the growing process. Older children can learn from them and perhaps not repeat the same mistakes. They can teach children that little bit more about the world around them and that life isn't all one big party or playtime – there are times when they have to take care. If they've been disobedient, rather than simply clumsy or unfortunate, accidents could also help them learn the lesson that mum or dad is right when it comes to looking after them. Parents are adults who know the world. They know best.

That's not to say any accident is welcome - of course it's not, and in some ways this view of life in the home rather misses the point. We'd all much prefer to hear laughter than tears, to see smiles and not sulks. And we'd certainly prefer to do without the agony, the drama, and the sheer terror of both child and parent that comes with a serious incident. We can never afford to be complacent about accidental injury.

We must always be vigilant to try to prevent them. We must never underestimate what our children might be able to do – always being one step ahead of them. They will be growing and developing so quickly at this stage that we must keep watching them carefully to see the new skills they are mastering – skills which could mean they are able to pull something down on top of them or reach for something we assumed was out of reach. It's also vital that all the equipment we buy is solid and well made, not just pretty. Look for a British Standard – (the letters BS and a number) on the label for cots, high chairs and buggies. If you can't afford new equipment, ask your health visitor's advice or look at the leaflets produced by the Child Accident Prevention Trust to check on safety points to look out for. Always try to get an instruction booklet or product information details when you buy second-hand. Protecting our young children has to be part of the deal on our side in return for their smiles, their trust, and their love. And if you think of the size of the problem, with more than one million children attending hospital casualty departments every year with injuries from accidents which could have been prevented, you see the scale of the change in attitude that's needed.

The last thing we mean by this is that if your child has an accident you have been, without question, negligent and have not been carrying out your proper duties as a parent. No one's perfect, mistakes can happen. And after all, children under 2 are at a dangerous age. They are gradually becoming mobile – they are beginning to crawl and walk –

and they are very, very inquisitive about the world around them – a world they are just beginning to learn about and which is totally fascinating to their developing minds. But their minds do not yet understand danger. These three factors together can be a lethal combination. That's why the role of parents is so crucial when their children are this age.

Yet many parents, while believing they are doing the best by their children, may be missing out on important safety guidelines which could provide a much more pain-free, trouble-free path to adulthood.

HOME AND AWAY

Very young children will spend the greatest amount of their time in their home, far more than older children. Not surprisingly, therefore, it's where the majority of accidents happen to them. So the home is where we must concentrate our efforts when thinking about child safety.

And just because we're thinking about and pinpointing the home and it's more likely that mothers will be at home with their children at this early age than fathers for most of the day, this doesn't mean that fathers don't play a vital part in keeping their young children's lives accident-free. They may well be less used to being with their babies and toddlers and less used to supervising them and taking care of them, but even if they chauvinistically feel it's not really their role to be involved in day-to-day childcare, they must learn as many safety rules as their partners. Unexpected circumstances or a sudden crisis could leave them in charge, which means they must know important information about protecting their children.

The thought of the inexperienced father fumbling about to find a pillow to place under his baby's head because mum's laid up with flu is enough to persuade any safety-conscious parent that the safety of children must be a joint affair. Pillows can suffocate small babies. Babies do not need pillows.

SUFFOCATION

Babies are more at risk of suffocation than older children, so beware of anything that looks like it might stop your very young child breathing normally. Remember, babies are less aware of the movements they make and so are less able to direct their arm and body movements. This means they cannot easily remove an obstacle – that pillow, for example – which is preventing them from breathing easily or at all. And they'll get weaker and weaker as they gasp for breath.

Also remember:

- Quilted sleeping bags can be dangerous for babies who can sometimes nestle too far down inside them. It may be an idea to fill the bottom of the bag with something soft such as a towel or small blanket to prevent this.

- Some babies have died in baby nests – quilted bags designed to keep a baby warm while being carried – because they've suffocated or become far too hot. Don't let them sleep in them. Buy a nest which meets the British Standard – BS 6595.

- Make sure material lining cots, prams, and safety bumpers is secure or your baby could be smothered by loose folds.

- Don't use cot-sized continental quilts for babies under 12 months. They could suffocate.

- Taking a tiny baby to bed with you for easy feeding is dangerous.

- Cats may want to snuggle into your baby's pram. This could easily suffocate her. Put a cat net over the pram if she's going to be outside.

- Don't allow your toddlers anywhere near polythene bags, plastic bags or clingfilm. They may be able to reach out and pick up a polythene bag which has been left on a chair or on the floor at a much earlier age than you imagine.

- Babies can suffocate in the pocket made by the fabric side of a mesh-type play-pen if the mesh side is left down. Keep it up at all times.

CHOKING

Very young children are also most in danger of choking. This is because their reflexes are not yet fully developed. If we choke we are usually strong enough to recover and our unconscious reflex means that as soon as there's any sign of danger we'll start coughing like fury to clear the throat. A baby does not have that immediate reflex and she may not have the strength in her movements to stop the choking by herself.

It's when children are around 6 months old that they discover their mouths and that's a pretty exciting find when you're first starting to learn about where you are and what you are! And into their mouths first go their fingers and their hands and later anything else they can find. So:

- Make sure baby toys, teats and dummies are intact and don't have any pieces which might crumble away from them.

- Make sure there are no loose press studs or buttons on your child's clothes or on yours which she could pull off and put into her mouth.

- Try not to let your very young child get hold of toys intended for your older children. That's a very easy way for harmless bits of Lego, counters from games or even a loose eye from a doll to turn into dangerous objects. The same goes for coins.

- Don't give fur fabric toys to children under 1 year old in case they chew off the fluff.

- Avoid pom poms on clothes near the neck. Your child could choke on them.

- Keep disposable nappies out of reach so babies cannot pull pieces off them and choke on them. Check the filling of the brand you use does not pull out easily.

- Don't prop a baby's bottle up and leave her to feed. She could easily choke. Don't leave a young child alone to feed in any case. And don't feed or give out drinks while travelling in a car or bus. The jolting could easily encourage choking.

- Don't give peanuts to a child under 5 years old. Not only can they choke, but the oil in the nut can cause swelling if it's trapped, which can lead to an attack of pneumonia.

- Be careful about giving your baby or toddler other hard substances which may be too much for the young to cope with. Boiled sweets are not a good idea, rusks are better than biscuits. Raw apple or raw carrot should be avoided for the first two years.

STRANGULATION

This is another danger area. But it's a danger quite easily avoided:

- Be careful not to tie a dummy or toy on a ribbon or a string more than 12 inches long to the side of a cot or a carry cot or play-pen, or to your baby's clothing, as it could twist and strangle her. Instead use a short length pinned on with a safety pin.

- Never tie a dummy round your baby's neck with ribbon or string or anything else.

- Cords or ribbons tied through the neck or hood of a cardigan or jumper can also be a danger. If the garment is knitted loosely or has an open weave, however pretty the pattern, it can catch on the side of a cot or pram and could also strangle.

Don't forget - the most common causes of accidental death in children who are less than one year old are choking on food, and suffocation and strangulation involving equipment, bedding or clothing. None of these precautions should be overlooked.

BURNING AND SCALDING

Again, the figures speak for themselves. Of the 40,000+ children who are burned in the home every year, three-quarters are under 5, the largest number of these being between 1 and 2 – the age of inquisitiveness and mobility but no understanding of danger. (Interestingly, surveys have shown that boys are twice as likely to be burned as girls).

Don't forget it only takes a couple of seconds for an accident to happen and never is that more immediately, dramatically and painfully demonstrated than with burning and scalding. The results can be minor, they can be major, they can kill. Children have died by climbing into baths of over-hot water when mum's attention was distracted, and mums will continually be surprised at how quickly their toddlers learn to climb. Make sure when yours manages to scale up her first mini-Everest there's nothing dangerous at the summit.

- The water in a kettle or teapot can scald up to half an hour after it has boiled. So can drinks half an hour after they're poured.

- A cup of tea can cause burns sufficient to require skin grafting up to 10 minutes after it's made.

Another surprise is how little it takes for an accident to be fatal. One 2-year-old farmer's daughter was burnt to death when she fell into a bucket of extremely hot water her elder brother was using on the farm. It's so easy to fail to realise quite how dangerous too much heat can be – and how easily it burns or scalds. So try to avoid burns by:

- Not panicking. In today's busy times we tend to stop everything we're doing and rush to answer a ringing phone or a knock at the door. If you're doing anything involving hot water or hot anything else, learn to keep calm and finish or make safe what you're doing, or remove your children from any danger area by taking them with you when you leave it. Missing a phone call is not a disaster when compared with a burnt child. If it's important, people always ring back.

- Not taking any chances. One mother left her baby, who was too young to crawl, in the middle of the living room. By rolling over he reached an electric fire, with its tempting bright red element, and burned himself on his forehead and hands.

And take note of these more specific measures:

- Always use a special, safety fireguard in front of any fire, fixed to the fireplace or the wall. This is vital even before your child starts to crawl. And never take off the guards which are fitted to gas and electric fires. Doing this would make it easier for a small child to grab hold of the hottest part of the heater. And don't forget the guard itself can burn, too.

- Don't hang or lean anything on a fireguard.

- Don't hang mirrors on the walls above fires. Children are fascinated by mirrors. An older child could get burned while trying to see; you could get burned while holding your child and that in turn could cause an accident.

- Buy flame-resistant night clothes and dressing gowns – all of these garments made in this country will be. Flimsy cotton is the most dangerous material for any article of clothing.

- Keep matches, lighters, lighted cigarettes and cigars, hot irons – and hot anything else – well away from children. And keep children well away from bonfires and fireworks before, during, and after they're lit. Never leave any of these things unattended. If you think you've put them far away out of reach, put them that bit further away. You can never be too careful.

- Don't leave a flex dangling from the iron which can be pulled at by an inquisitive toddler, yanking the iron from its 'safe' hiding place.

- The rule about flex applies to kettles and any other appliances which could burn or scald. Self-coiling flexes should preferably be fitted. Of course, the appliances should be kept well out of reach. We've heard of one 10-month-old baby who died as a result of pulling a kettle of hot water over himself.

- Steam can scald: don't leave kettles simmering.

- Remember, food and hot drinks – and the containers they both come in – can burn and scald. Keep well away from little fingers.

- Don't hold a hot drink while also holding a baby – one sudden movement could be disastrous.

- Don't pass or hold a hot drink or hot plate of food above the head of your child.

- Don't use tablecloths which hang down so children can pull at the sides, maybe pulling scalding food or drink with them. In any case keep hot drinks away from the edges of tables, and use mugs rather than cups as they are less easily knocked over.

- Don't hold your child near the stove where she could reach out and grab a hot pan or touch a hot gas or electric ring. Where possible use back rings. Get into the habit of turning pan handles away from the edges of cookers and work tops. A cooker should preferably have a work top next to it so you do not have to carry hot pans across the kitchen. If you're busy at the stove, leave your child in a play-pen.

- Oven doors which open downwards can be dangerous if a toddler stands on them, tilting the oven, or whatever's cooking, on top of herself.

- Never leave any hot container or appliance on top of a wobbly chair or table, or on top of a fridge, freezer or cooker where doors are opened and closed.

- Always put cold water in first when you're running a bath and don't have your hot water thermostat set too high (more than 54° centigrade or 130° Fahrenheit). For your child the water should be warm, not hot. Hot could easily scald. If you have mixer taps, run a splash of cold water through after you've turned the hot off to make sure your child won't get burnt on the tap itself. Don't add hot water while your child is in the bath. And remember, toddlers have died when they've climbed into baths meant for older people – or have been placed in them by 'helpful' older brothers or sisters. A baby or toddler should never be in the bathroom when you're not there.

POISONING

Estimated number of poisonings in the home	
Age	*Number*
0 - 2	**27,636**
3 - 4	**8,957**

Children under the age of two are at by far the greatest risk of poisoning. Remember, a baby cannot discriminate between nice and nasty tastes.

Symptoms which show your child may have swallowed something poisonous include:

- Losing consciousness
- Confusion
- Stomach pains

- Skin burns
- Vomiting
- Staining of the skin around the mouth

If your child has taken anything, take what's left or a sample of the substance to the doctor or hospital with you but don't delay by searching round for it.

This is an important time to keep dangerous substances out of reach: the most common age for accidental poisoning by medicines is 2 years, and the most common age for accidental poisoning by non-medicines is 1 year old. In many cases of accidental poisoning the parent is using the substance at the time. In some cases the parent actually administers the poison by mistake. They may give, for example, surgical spirit, mistaking it for gripe water.

Again, the key to safety is not to underestimate what your child can do, and what it might occur to her to eat or drink. Perfume, cough mixture, sleeping pills, and hair remover are some of the substances the very youngest are known to have sampled. Toddlers have reached far beyond where their parents dreamed they could have reached; they've found what was thought to be unfindable. So:

- Keep all types of medication out of reach and locked away. If you can't buy a lockable medicine cabinet, use a kitchen cupboard with a safety catch. Take care that any visitors don't leave pills or medicines in handbags, in jacket pockets, on bedside tables or anywhere else youngsters, left just for a moment, could find them. You may have to ask the chemist for child-resistant tops – but remember, some children have been able to open these so they are not necessarily completely childproof.

- Don't keep even one jar of pills or bottle of medicine out for convenience's sake. Most of the accidents involving medication happen in the mornings, which could indicate that the toddler gets hold of it just after mum or dad has finished with it.

- Blister packs in which the pills can't be seen, and foil strip packs, are more difficult for children to get into – but not impossible.

- Remember that medicines you buy over the counter such as iron tablets or aspirin can be as dangerous as prescription drugs.

- Don't take pills in front of your children. At the age of 18 months and more they may want to copy.

- Keep all cleaning substances out of reach. Buy brands with child-resistant tops, but still make sure they can't be got at. Never put bleach or any other dangerous liquid into a lemonade or soft drink bottle.

- Toddlers have also been known to drink shampoo and bubble bath, record cleaning fluid, weedkiller, rat poison, white spirit, nail varnish and perfume, and eat shaving cream and nappy sanitising powder. At around 15 or 18 months most youngsters will be walking alone exploring every cupboard they can find – but how can you be sure yours won't start even earlier? So fit child-resistant catches to kitchen cupboards.

- Don't use bleach and lavatory cleaner together – they can combine to give off dangerous fumes.

- Start teaching even toddlers what's banned and what's not. The garden shed or anywhere else where paraffin, paint thinners, plant sprays and the like are kept are most definitely out of bounds.

- Don't pick blackberries, mushrooms, or any other safe foods from your garden or the countryside in front of your toddler. It's best if they're not encouraged to put anything growing outdoors into their mouths. They won't know what's good for them and what's bad.

- Remember, alcohol is very bad for small children and to them it looks similar to the stuff they usually drink. Don't leave it anywhere they can reach it and never leave a half-empty glass around.

- Beware dogs' faeces, which can cause *toxicara canis* – and that can lead to blindness. Don't let them play with the mess, and ensure they wash hands thoroughly after they've played in sandpits or grass.

FALLS

Falls are a serious hazard for the very young. In fact the most typical profile of a child injured while at play is that of a 2-year-old boy who falls and cuts himself on the head or face.

Of course the oops-a-daisy variety of tumble is usually more of a fright than a danger to babies and many lighter falls cause no more damage than a few tears.

But did you know?

- In the first few months of an infant's life, the major risk she faces from an accident is from other people dropping her.

- The most common non-fatal accidents involving children less than 12 months old are falls.

- Every year around fifty children of all ages die from a fall in the home.

Important rules to remember are:

- Never leave a small baby where she might roll off any sort of surface while you're changing her, dressing her, preparing her for a bath or anything else. Most accidents at changing time happen when the child falls off a changing unit or raised surface. Remember, a baby can't fall off the floor: it might be better to leave her there!

- Don't put your baby in any sort of bouncing cradle on any surface other than the floor.

- Always supervise your baby in her bouncing cradle and do the straps up.

- Always do up harnesses on push chairs and high chairs. Don't leave your baby unattended in either.

- Put safety gates up to stop toddlers getting to stairs. Most deaths which result from falling on or down stairs are of children aged between 1 and 4 years old. Teach them, as soon as they are able, to climb down stairs backwards, on their tummies, and always to take care on stairs. Beware especially banisters with horizontal bars, and those with vertical bars more than 10 cm (4 inches) apart. These should be boarded up.

- Take care that floors aren't slippery – you could crush your small baby if you fell over while holding her.

- Most accidents with backpacks (which look like rucksacks with frames and allow you to carry babies who can support their own backs and necks) and slings (soft pouches which you strap on to yourself and which hold your baby) happen when parents fall while carrying their baby.

- Make sure your windows can't be opened too wide so children can't climb out. Try not to put chairs or anything else a child might climb on near a window. Fit safety catches to upstairs windows, keeping the keys to them in a safe place in case of fire or another emergency.

- Beware of balconies. These too might need boarding up or covering with wire netting if there's any danger of children climbing them. Also keep away any plant pots or anything else a child could use to climb on to reach over a balcony. Children shouldn't be allowed on balconies by themselves.

DROWNING

Children love water – but they can drown in only 2 inches of it. And the very young are especially vulnerable. If they find themselves submerged their first reaction is more likely to be to yell for help rather than to move to where they might find air. Valuable seconds – sometimes valuable lives – have been lost. Young children must be watched and guarded so closely when they are near any form of water, from the bath, to a pond, to a canal, to a swimming pool ... to a fish tank.

Take care to remember these precautions:

- Use a non-slip bath mat. Don't let your toddler stand up in the bath without holding on to her.

- Never leave your baby or young toddler alone in a bath or basin even for a second. In fact they shouldn't be alone in the bathroom at all. A young child can even drown in some lavatories.

- Keep a watchful eye on young children paddling. At this age, never let them go alone. Empty paddling pools as soon as the children finish playing.

- Teach them to swim as early as possible but remember, rubber rings and other inflatable aids do not necessarily stop your child drowning. For example, she may tip upside down and would then be trapped. Never let children under 8 swim unsupervised.

- If you've a garden pond, cover it with strong mesh or fence it off. If you're visiting people with a garden pond, anywhere very near it should be out of bounds and you must still be ever vigilant.

- Take special care when you're on holiday and may be tempted to be more relaxed and less vigilant and alert. You can never afford that luxury with a young baby or toddler around.

CUTS

Even at this early age, glass is a danger, not so much for the baby but certainly for the toddler just starting to walk. Because she'll be uncertain and unsteady on her feet, she's more likely to topple over and that could be very dangerous if she's managed to get her hands on anything made of glass. In any case, keep glass objects away from young, grabbing hands. In addition:

- Keep any sharp object, including scissors, razors, and knives, well away. When you're using them get into the habit of showing your child safe practices, such as always holding scissors with the points downwards when you're passing them to someone. Children will already be starting to copy what you do.

- Keep an eye on toys to make sure there are no sharp edges or points on them.

- With glass doors and French windows, make sure they have safety glass fitted - this is glass which is specially toughened or laminated and much safer. Otherwise cover doors and windows with special plastic film. It isn't adequate just to mark dangerous glass by sticking bright shapes or strips on it to remind the children it's there – children often don't look where they're going and at 18 months to 2 years of age it's likely your child will be beginning to run around but won't be able to avoid obstacles. It's fine to board up the glass in low doors and windows.

- Don't allow your toddler to run around with anything sharp such as a pencil (she could be drawing by now) or lolly stick in her mouth.

BABYWALKERS - A note of caution.

Babywalkers cause more accidents among young children than any other single item of equipment. Our advice is: don't let your young children use babywalkers. They will give a child who can't yet walk the ability to move around very, very fast and this can be a menace – especially in a kitchen, near a glass door or near the top of stairs. They allow them to be much more mobile than a one or two year old would usually be and to rush around finding, if your luck is out, something you've mistakenly left lying around which might cause them harm. They can easily wheel into someone carrying something hot or sharp. In any case research shows babywalkers do not encourage children's development. A child using one will not learn to walk any the faster.

IN THE CAR

Around 10,000 child passengers are injured in car accidents every year – and around 75 are killed. Around 300 babies are killed or injured in cars. These figures could easily be reduced if necessary safety precautions were put into practice by everyone:

- Make sure your child is safely restrained from the very first ride home from hospital. By doing this you can dramatically cut down the risk of a serious injury in any crash.

- Babies must never be carried in mum's arms, especially in the front seat. Never put a seat belt around yourself and your baby – she could be crushed in the event of an accident.

- Babies who are less than a year old should be in a rear-facing infant carrier held in place by an adult's diagonal and lap seat belt – this is seen as the safest option. Otherwise they should be in a carrycot fastened by restraints in the back of the car, with the cot cover in place so they cannot be thrown out. This must be the rule from their first journey away from hospital and from then on. You cannot rely on the driving skills of others.

- Toddlers aged 1 and over (and possibly slightly younger) should be belted into a child safety seat which is properly fastened to the back of a car by an anchorage kit or an adult seat belt.

- If you only have one child the safest place for a child restraint is in the middle of the back seat; the next safest is anywhere else on the back seat. If need be, it can be fitted on to the front seat.

- Never let a young child stand or sit without restraint in the front of a car – you will be breaking the law and risking their lives.

- Never let a child stand on the back seat, lean out of a window, or try to distract the driver.

- Make sure adults and heavy loads are strapped up too. In an accident your bodies can be thrown around and you could be turned into a missile which would crush anything in its way.

- Use child safety locks.

- Never, never, never, leave a baby or young child by herself in a car while you pop away. There's a risk of babysnatching, a risk of suffocation, of choking if she's sick while you're away, a risk of overheating if it's a hot day. That's far too many risks.

AND IN ADDITION...

- Don't let your toddler play with electric plugs and points.

- Even if your baby or toddler has a cold, don't use a movable electric fire in the bathroom.

- Babies often injure themselves by biting on the hooks of coathangers. Don't let them.

- Dogs may be unfriendly – don't teach your child to trust and pat any dog that comes along.

- Take care of your child in a playground. Swings can easily bump into the very young causing nasty injuries. Don't let your attention be swayed by chats with other mums.

- Harnesses might be a good idea. They keep a toddler's hands free which means the child can walk more steadily.

- If you are carrying your baby in a backpack or a sling which holds the baby on your back, be careful when using trains that automatic doors don't close on your child, especially if the tops of the doors curve inwards as they do on London tube trains. However most accidents with slings and backpacks are the result of a parent falling while carrying the baby.

- If there are sharp edges in your home, tie cardboard or that bubbled plastic packaging round them, or you can buy special safety smooth edges. When he was 2, our son cut himself badly when running in the kitchen and into an old-fashioned gas stove.

- Interestingly, the sitting room is the most dangerous room in the house, with most accidents happening there.

- Play pens are worth their weight in gauze! Provided they conform to safety standards and are more than 2 feet high, you know when the phone rings or the door bell goes that there's somewhere safe to put your child. Accidents are most likely to happen when you're under stress or in a hurry.

- British Standards are most important for all your equipment, but especially cots, prams, pushchairs, fireguards and toys.

- Most home accidents occur in April and May, the least occur in November and December. But that doesn't mean you can be less vigilant, especially around Christmas time when there could be extra flexes trailing and more alcohol, excitement and choke-inducing goodies around.

- Take special care to avoid accidents in other people's homes, especially if they are not homes used to young children.

- You should always know where your 0–2 year old is – and that should be in her play pen, in her cot or pram ... or in the same room as you.

We cannot hope to cover every single accident prevention measure here, but excellent leaflets *Keep Your Baby Safe*, *Keep Them Safe*, and *First Ride Safe Ride* are available from the Child Accident Prevention Trust, whose address is listed at the back of this book.

It would be wrong and naïve to assume that the only threat to our smallest children comes from accidents. Horrific cases of non- accidental injury are never that far from our televisions screens and the pages of our newspapers and magazines. If you suspect your partner is beating your child, your first priority must be to protect the child, not the batterer. Your child is an innocent with only you to rely on. You must not let her down.

There's no doubt that many young children, especially crying babies who do not understand you and who cannot tell you what's wrong, can be very frustrating to care for. If you feel you're being driven to your wits' end, you must seek help. Go to your doctor, to your health visitor, to a friend or relation, to another new mother, to CRY-SIS, the support group for mothers with crying babies ... to the Samaritans if need be. But do not take your frustrations out on your baby, if for no other reason than that you'll never forgive yourself.

And finally, take care about the childminders and babysitters you allow to take care of your baby or toddler. Make sure childminders are registered, and make sure babysitters are aged 16 or over, are recommended by someone you trust or have references which satisfy you. Leave numbers where you can be reached – and an address in case the phone where you'll be is out of order. And leave your doctor's phone number next to the phone or leave it somewhere prominent with details of how to get to the nearest phone box.

You cannot afford to take any chances when it comes to the health and wellbeing of your baby.

Chapter Three
COMMUNICATING WITH YOUR 0-2 YEAR OLD

Your youngster's heading towards the glass you've just dropped which has shattered all over the kitchen floor. You don't ask her not to touch. You don't explain she might get hurt. You don't suggest that nasty lacerations to her arms and hands might result from her badly-judged attempt to grasp at the pretty, twinkling fragments round about her. One word, and one word only, is all you need. That word is 'No'.

The reason you need just that one word is not solely because precious seconds will be lost if you try to add to your instinctive command. It's more than that. In that situation and in any other potentially dangerous situations, there is no argument and there is no debate. You are in charge. Your very young child does not need explanations, she does not need to understand why you are saying what you are saying. All she has to do is to accept that you're right.

That's not to say you should be dictatorial. But the message that should come from you – and it's a caring message, not a threatening one – is that mum's in charge, mum knows best, mum is looking after you. And that's because she is a grown-up and knows the world. Toddlers do not know the world, and so they do not have a say, any say, in matters of safety. Very young children tend to ignore warnings and instructions. This is one warning they must not ignore.

And it's one word you must only use when you mean it and can carry through your instruction. Your child should stop when she hears it, then you should lift her away. Never say 'No' in that firm, definite way and then allow the child to carry on with whatever it was she was doing.

It's a word she may not understand in its literal sense. To her it may just sound like a noise. But she will understand what you mean because of the *way* you say it – just as a dog or cat might. The sound and tone of your voice, your facial expression and the movement your body makes, will combine to tell a baby or small children what you are desperate for them to understand. They are to stop and not to touch anything. At this age they will learn more from your body language and even from your feelings than they will from anything you actually say.

FEELINGS

But it's not just warning signs that your baby can read in your voice and your face. They can tell more than we imagine by our expressions and by the feelings that come across from us. We can communicate care, concern and protection if we give them lots of hugs and attention. We can communicate to them that we love them and value them as independent little people in their own right if we show them lots of affection and delight in the things they do.

And communicating those positive feelings to your children at their earliest ages is very, very important. Few experts doubt that giving children a secure and happy beginning to their lives and showing them support and love throughout their formative years will help give them more security and stability throughout their lives. It will also help you gain your child's trust – it will help her to realise that she can trust your reactions, that you can understand her wants and needs. And that might be vital for her future safety.

Let's go back to that situation we mentioned at the end of Chapter One. Your child has been approached by a stranger. Does she go with him? If she's confident and secure in the belief that she's cared for at home, if she knows she can trust the messages you send her and if your message is not to go with strangers, the chances are she won't.

IT'S NEVER TOO LATE

That's not to say that if parents don't communicate brilliantly with their children very early on, then all's lost and their children are about to be scooped up by a molester or kidnapper. We can't reiterate often enough that no parent is perfect, or should hope to be. We must all try to do our best – that is, after all, the best we can do. And it's never too late to make friends with your child and show her you want to communicate with her in the true sense of the word.

But it makes sense to begin that communication process as early as possible and that is as soon as your child is born. It's far from easy, especially for a first-time mum or dad, but it is worth spending time on and concentrating on, especially if you're starting to worry that you will remember his or her early years as a mound of nappies and an earful of screams. It will benefit you too and help you gain more from the whole experience.

GETTING TO KNOW YOUR BABY

It's easy for the first months – even the first years – of being a parent to pass by almost without giving you time to enjoy it. You'll be in a new financial situation, a new situation with your partner. There'll be more housework, more to pack into each day and more to worry about. But don't forget to give time to the new individual in your family – not just to the added chores her arrival means.

You need to get to know her and develop a relationship with her. A baby is trying to communicate in many ways which parents may not realise. A baby may try to communicate in verbal ways, although obviously not in a language we recognise. She might be saying 'I'm happy', 'I'm in pain', or 'I'm tired'. She may also be trying to communicate by crying and it's important for you to try to distinguish the different crying sounds she makes. There's the pain cry which is a high pitched noise, then a rest, another scream and a rest. There's the hunger cry which is more rhythmic. There's the tired cry which is an on-and-off whimper. There are also boredom cries and lonely cries. Working out which is which will give you both a quieter life.

There are also the more pleasant noises for you to enjoy which will help you get to know your baby. If she is babbling and you babble back – even if it's while you're doing the ironing – you'll be keeping her happy and you'll be communicating with her in her way.

Keeping a close watch on your child will also help you stop some of the crying before it starts. You will be able to spot when your child is preparing to start and hopefully intervene in time. Often if a baby has had enough – maybe of being held, or of being played with, or of being held by someone who is not mum – her eye direction will start to stray away. Then she'll start agitating her arms and legs and then the face will start to go and the crying will start. Watch closely, really get to know your child, and you may be able to stop that process. It's not easy. Things that please and displease your baby are changing all the time as she grows, changes and develops.

It's often been said that you shouldn't always attend to a baby when she cries – you'll be spoiling her and she'll never learn to be properly independent. But that is not the case for very young babies. Any baby 6 months old or less will be crying because of a biological need. She is not old enough to know how to try to manipulate her parents and demand attention or to know how to wind you up. She will be crying because she needs to. There is a reason for it within her own body. It could be pain, or hunger, or discomfort. It's certainly something she is powerless to control and she needs your help. You cannot 'spoil' a very young baby. And if you leave a baby crying, that in itself can cause discomfort and pain for her.

As your baby grows it becomes more important to ensure that she starts to develop some independence. After all, the process of growing up is simply the process of evolving into a separate human being with a life of one's own. You will have an urge to do everything for your baby and to protect her, but even at this stage it's not too early to let your child start to do things for herself. It won't be much, of course. But it's been suggested that if she's trying to reach out for something, a toy for example, rather than giving it to her or guiding it into her hand, it might be better to allow her to keep trying and finally succeed in reaching it by herself. This means that already you'll have started to beat off the 'What can I do for her?' attitude which can swamp some children. Instead your attitude is growing into, 'What can I let her do for herself?'. Psychologists have suggested that you help your baby roll over or reach for something only when she gets frustrated or angry. They add that when she's a bit bigger, if she wants to try to feed herself, let her, but cover everything that could get messed up so it doesn't mean too much work for you. If she wants to put her own boots on, try to have patience and allow her the time to do it.

At a younger age, maybe around 6 months, your baby will realise she is a separate entity and may start to panic when you're not there. It's important to reassure her that you are there (you are maybe in the next room) but it's also important to encourage her to have some independence, to play by herself at times and sleep in her cot in a separate room at times. If your toddler is very clingy, this is something which can be encouraged for short spaces of time and can then be followed by lots of praise if, say, she's been playing well on her own for five minutes.

DON'T UNDERESTIMATE

So that's the beginning of the process of growing up and growing into a separate individual. It's a process which will need a lot of your attention. Don't forget, babies are very active learners. We all learn all the time through our relations with other people, and babies are very close to adults for a very high proportion of their time. Your child will be growing all the time in all senses of the word.

She will understand more than you think and sense more than you think. She will know if her mum's uncertain and lacks confidence. She'll know this partly through the messages she's getting from her mother's attitude and partly through the routine which runs her life. She'll know if her mum's disorganised and unsure about decisions – babies who've cried and cried have often improved when the routine around them, of feeding, cleaning, sleeping, playing, is tightened up. And she'll sense anxiety in the way she's being held if mum has very little confidence in herself. Babies should be held firmly but lovingly, not in a way in which you'd expect to behave with a rare but dangerous animal that you don't want to injure because of its value and you really don't feel happy about holding.

BE CONSISTENT

Children are generally much better at grasping the feelings of their parents than most of us imagine. One mother told us about the time she returned home after a very bad day at work. She was trying to be 'a good mother' on her return, asking her little boy all the right questions while doing the washing up. Her son said to her, 'Are you angry with me?'. She assured him that she wasn't. But he said, 'You've got an angry face, mum.' And he was right. She was wound up, although it wasn't because of anything her little boy had done. Children younger than that will also feel the anger but they won't be able to express themselves. This can confuse them. If a mother is telling her child to 'Come here', but her body language and facial expression is telling the child that she doesn't want her to, the child will be confused and not know what to do.

They may react to what you look like, not to what you're saying. The messages you send your children must be consistent if you want them to be obedient when it really matters.

It's understandable if parents sometimes don't stop to think about how their moods are affecting their very small children – we aren't different people just because we've suddenly given birth. We'll have many of the same thoughts and preoccupations. But it is important to remember that children are, as one expert has said, like blotting paper. They soak up the emotions around them. Even very young children can feel anger in the air – and positive, optimistic feelings, too. This is important generally in the household and more specifically when you relate to your baby. So be honest about your own feelings. If you're feeling stressed or depressed don't keep it to yourself. Talk to someone about it. There's nothing wrong with seeking some support and sympathy.

How you look and how you sound are very important for a new born baby. From 1 month old, your child should be able to recognise her mother. That's pretty quick learning. Talk to a very young baby and the baby will respond by smiling and later joining in, after a fashion! No, she doesn't understand what you are saying but your presence reassures and fascinates her. If a mother is depressed and looks away without trying to communicate, the child will start to be depressed too. She won't have anything to respond to.

So expression and the sound coming from you are, in your child's early years, probably more important in communicating your message than what you're actually saying – although there would be no point in talking in gibberish! We do, of course, want our children to develop speaking skills to enable them to communicate with us exactly what they want to say.

This may all help us develop sound relationships with our children early in their lives. But there is another area to examine to try to ensure that our safety messages will reach their destinations when they are really needed.

YOUR CHILD'S WORLD

Early on in your child's life, the most important lesson for a parent to learn is to be fair. And it's not fair to blame and tell off a child under 1 year old if she puts herself in a dangerous situation – and certainly not if she has an accident when she'll already be frightened enough. In fact it's not fair to tell a 1-year-old off for anything. She is too young to understand the implications of her actions or much about the world around her. So if a baby pulls something heavyish down on top of her because she wants to pull herself up, it's not her fault. She's just trying to explore and develop herself and test out what her body can do. That's natural. It's your responsibility to try to make sure there's nothing near her cot or her pram, or wherever she is, which could possibly cause her harm – remembering to think one step ahead of her and what she may be able to achieve. Crouch down and see how tempting that ornament looks from down below. See why youngsters climb on to window ledges – they can see the sky and the outside world from where they are but only a tiny bit of it. Is it surprising they want to explore further? It's up to you to see what they might want to do and to help them achieve it safely. A child this young has no concept of danger. Her world is centred on herself and on nothing else.

WHAT ARE YOUR PRIORITIES?

The young toddler also knows nothing about danger and again, it's up to you to take care and protect. Let's go back to the child at the beginning of this chapter. How do we ensure that she obeys your command and doesn't reach out for the glass before you can reach her and scoop her out of danger? The key to this has to be in your use of the word 'No' and in how often you use it.

As a parent you must develop very early on in your new career a sense of priority. You must decide what is important and what is not so important. Hopefully you will have safety at the top of your first list.

We believe that the special voice that every parent uses to shout the word 'No' at a child about to do something wrong or bad should be used sparingly – only, in fact, when the child is in danger. If you are always using a screaming pitch every time your child goes to pick her nose or drops her beaker, your message will lose its power. You will find yourself in the same position as the boy who cried 'Wolf'. When something really dangerous comes along your child might be more blasé about your warning. It's natural that at this time in her life she may be starting to see how far she can get and trying to work out the boundaries of her behaviour. And if she remembers she didn't come to any harm last time, when she dropped her beaker and you shouted 'No', hearing your warning again may have little effect.

THERE IS AN ALTERNATIVE

So if she's sitting in her high chair and keeps dropping her rusk on the floor, why not treat it as a game? Pick it up for her and wait for her to drop it again. There's no need for raised voices or tempers. And when you've had enough of that game, take the rusk away with a jolly, 'All finished', and distract her attention with something else. Maybe put her in the play pen with some new toys in different shapes and colours to prevent her being bored. If she does seem to be grizzly and irritable without good cause, maybe rearrange your schedule and go for a walk with her. Distraction is always better than confrontation.

This means that if, for example, your child is scribbling on the floor with a crayon, you should remove the crayon and replace it with an alternative toy which she does know how to use appropriately. Save the crayons for an occasion when you have time to show her how to use them properly. We think it's best to ignore naughty behaviour which isn't dangerous or serious and not punish it, instead diverting attention away to something not seen as 'naughty'.

TIME OUT

If you feel you do need to discipline your child in some way, more sensible than raising your voice or smacking her if she isn't in a dangerous situation, is to opt for the Time Out method of coping with it. If you feel you're at the end of your tether, you're really agitated and you might hit her, simply say, 'That's enough', and raise your hand. You switch off attention from what she's doing until she's being good. You could put her in the corner of the room and ignore her for a few minutes, or if she's a bit older and not too clingy, put her in a safe room for a few minutes and close the door. Your message is, 'Mummy will come for you when you're ready to be good'. And when she is good later on, tell her how pleased you are and give her a cuddle.

For the first couple of times, she'll probably cry through her Time Out. But then she'll realise you will be coming back to her, you haven't gone for ever, or you won't be ignoring her for ever. When the time's over you just carry on with the day's activities. Don't smack her, as she'll have stopped playing up by then and that would confuse her – she'll think, 'I've stopped but mummy's still hit me'. The message you should be getting across to her through all of this is that you're still there for her, you object to what she was doing and you stopped her doing it and you expect her to behave better from now on. It will also give you time to have a breather and to wind down.

The 'No' warning doesn't only have to be saved for absolute emergencies. It can also be used in a preventative way. If your youngster starts pulling at the fur of your pet dog the animal might be used to this particular brand of play and not object. But a less friendly dog in the park might – and could bark, growl or, worse, bite in return. So say 'No' and raise your hand in the way a policeman does to stop oncoming traffic when she starts on your pet dog. Your child may be surprised and may start to cry, so give her a cuddle to show that by stopping she's done the right thing, you're pleased with her and that you had her interests at heart.

It's important as well to give her lots of praise when she's being good. Soon she'll learn what's coming next as soon as you raise your hand and say 'That's enough', and she'll stop misbehaving. There's been no shouting, no screaming, no raised voices even. That will be saved for when something really serious might have to be avoided.

It's also never too early to say, 'Don't do that, it will hurt you', or 'Ouchy, ouchy', if you prefer. That's the next stage. It's not only giving your child an instruction, it's also giving her a reason. As your child gets older you can give more complex, elaborate reasons, but for now that will do.

And it's never too early to think about getting safety messages across in other ways. Children of all ages learn by example; they'll be picking things up from your behaviour all the time. If your younger toddler is already at the stage of copying some of the things you do, by playing with her own plastic pots and pans as you do the cooking for example, why not extend this by extending your 'Ouchy, ouchy' message to her pretend pots. You'll find it's a pretty good game! If a spark flies out of the fire and glows on the carpet, a grimace and an 'Ouchy, ouchy' from you should begin to get the message across on that, too, or on any other potential hazard.

DON'T DO AS I DO...?

It's important to get into the habit of changing your own modes of behaviour, remembering that your child will soon – or will now – be watching you and preparing to copy your actions. Try to start keeping to the Green Cross Code and other road safety rules when you're crossing a road. Of course you'll take greater care when crossing with a pram or push-chair anyway and it may seem very boring to take all the precautions even then. But it's sensible to get into the habit and to leave your jay-walking days behind you.

Set your own road safety rules, too. They'll be different now you've got a new baby. Don't stick your pram or push-chair into the road and then look to see if there's traffic on its way. Yes, your visibility will be reduced because you are standing behind whatever it is your child's riding in, but that doesn't mean you should put your child in danger. If you've another youngster as well as your small baby, set safety rules for her too. If she's on a bike you should make her get off and walk with you holding your hand – the whole family crossing together. Do this even on small, quiet roads. It will be good training for the big ones.

You may have to adapt other parts of your behaviour and stop doing things which are actually safe for adults to do but which would not be safe for a child to copy. Take dad warming himself, hands behind his back, in front of the fire, for example. It's totally safe for him, but not safe at all for a child who will be less able to judge distance than a grown-up and who may be less steady on her feet.

This is also true of things which aren't so safe for adults to do either – such as smoking cigarettes. Very young children are very impressionable. And don't argue about this in front of them. On all safety issues, try to keep a united front or you'll draw attention to the dangers in a way that might make your child inquisitive.

When it comes to clearing up that broken glass we've been mentioning, most adults could pick up the largest pieces by hand and would probably be tempted to if there wasn't a child about. But don't do this if there are children present. Glass is such an attractive thing for them to reach for, and it's hard enough to prevent them from doing this without your bad example to confuse them.

Both parents must agree on this. If a child, even at this young age, sees dad doing something mum has told her is dangerous, she'll be puzzled and wonder who to believe. She may not take it for granted that you're telling her the truth when she hears the next safety message you come out with. Children are very logical. They notice things, they like things to make sense. A lot of under 2s are very bright. Don't underestimate them.

Chapter Four
DANGERS FACED BY THE 2-5 YEAR OLD

Your child's growing up, learning and developing right in front of your eyes. Every day will bring new adventures and new experiences for her in the world she's discovering around her. She'll be able to do more and more for herself, from putting her toys away to eating an apple. And that takes your job in keeping her safe one step further.

THE SHIFT IN RESPONSIBILITY

The reason for this is that she's developing a degree of independence, even if it's only a small step in that direction. This in turn means you will soon have to start encouraging her to see that keeping safe and secure is partly her responsibility, even if it's only a small part.

Consider this cautionary tale. A young mother is out shopping with her younger son in a push-chair and her 3-year-old by her side. With fifty different things on her mind, from what she is going to cook for dinner to when the gas boiler might be repaired, she waits on the kerbside until there is a decent gap in the traffic. Then she starts to walk across. What she hasn't noticed is that her 3-year-old has lagged behind (something very dangerous in itself – he should have been holding her hand or holding on to the side of the push-chair). When he reaches the kerb, he spots his mum who's almost reached the other side of the road, and steps out to be with her. At that very moment a car zooms up, as if out of nowhere, and knocks him down.

Amazingly he isn't seriously hurt. But there is an important lesson in this for all parents. As his mother explains; 'The earliest safety message he had received was to be with mum. He had learned to be with me. He trusted me to take care of him and to take responsibility for him. He thought being safe meant being with me. His road safety message was to stay with me. I made a mistake by crossing the road without him – and I hadn't allowed for that. Parents don't make it clear when they expect the child to be responsible.'

In other words, when our children are very small we have to take total responsibility for their safety as they don't understand danger. As they grow up we have to start to encourage them to take some of that responsibility for themselves if or when the situation demands it.

That doesn't mean we should allow them independence to run riot, or independence to make choices about how to run their lives. Of course they are far too young for that. And we should never engineer a scenario of the sort described above. No child of that age or older can be relied upon to make an adult decision about whether and when to cross the road or whether to wait for mum. In any case, it wouldn't be good for the mental health, stress levels, or blood pressure of the anxious parent waiting at the far side of the road. But there are ways, which we will outline in the next chapter, in which we can try to encourage the beginnings of independence in a pre-schooler and this will reap further benefits as he or she grows first into a teenager and then an adult, and meets new challenges and undoubtedly new dangers.

In the meantime, your child is still very much a child. She'll need your guidance, your help and your love. And she'll still need you to do your utmost to ensure that her environment is a safe one.

BE CONSISTENT

Many new parents will be discovering that this period in your child's life includes the dreaded toddler tantrum stage. So often you may feel tempted to give in to quieten that terrible screaming and whining. But it's important that you *never* give in on safety matters, and that you stay firm. If it's not a safety matter it's worth trying to think whether the issue which caused your youngster such frustrations could have been avoided. Again, it's particularly important that your safety message is streamlined, with both parents agreeing on all aspects of it, along with anyone else who may be caring for your child for shorter periods. That way your child won't be getting confusing messages – just the one, unchanging set of rules.

If, for example, your child is always 'belted-up' with all the right safety equipment when she's in your car although she complains about it constantly, you've got to think carefully about what will happen if she's in her grandmother's car which doesn't have a child safety seat. If you don't remove the safety seat from your car and strap it to granny's, your child will be confused that a rule applies to one car but not to another – and it will also give her extra ammunition when she's objecting to the belts and ties and straps. After all, just about every child hates being strapped in.

Sometimes your child may try to break the safety rules you're setting as part of her way of exploring her world and trying to make sense of it – she'll want to see what your reactions might be. But it's all too easy for a busy, harassed parent to assume that is the motive for all her wrong doings. There are plenty of other reasons why youngsters put themselves in danger and it's certainly not always the case that they do it to make your life all the more difficult. You can tell her not to touch dog mess as often as you want, but if there's a prize conker or a pretty leaf slap bang in the middle of a large chunk of the stuff, disobedience will not be her reason for breaking your rules. It will be her natural inquisitiveness and interest. If you've told her time and time again not to run when she's on the (often slippery) surround to a swimming pool and she doesn't do as she's told, slips and falls over (and are there any children who haven't done this?) she hasn't done it to terrify the life out of you. She's probably done it because the excitement of the moment and the atmosphere of the place, coupled with the sight of all those other boys and girls running about to copy, has put all other messages from her mind.

SAFETY FIRST

It's undoubtedly true that as a general rule accident prevention doesn't come high enough on the list of priorities. Parents assume they are taking enough precautions but they're not. Remember, for all children in this country older than 6 months, accidents are the biggest cause of death - not disease, not illness. But there is still a sense of complacency amongst parents - the feeling that children will learn from having accidents, even that it will help them grow into tougher adults. That's a very negative way of looking at life. It's a harsh world we live in if children only learn from bad experiences.

As babies grow into toddlers, child safety doesn't become more important – it's always important – but it does become more complicated and it does cover more areas. As children grow older they can do more, they think more, they have more reasons for doing things which can upset the safe environment we are trying to create. But it's still vital we do our utmost to try.

HOMES AND GARDENS

The older pre-school child will spend less time in the home than the small baby, but again that's no reason to be complacent. Remember the figures we gave you in Chapter Two: 3 to 4-year-olds suffer 150,900 accidents a year at home, a statistic which includes far too many child deaths. It's a smaller figure than for children aged 2 and under but it's still an awful lot of pain and hurt for children and an awful lot of distress and guilt for parents.

Apart from the guidelines directly relating to baby equipment, all of the rules we've already outlined concerning safety in the home will still apply. Your child is older and stronger but she can still be drowned or burned, she can still fall, choke, suffocate, or be electrocuted. Many parents feel pleased with themselves if they strap their child securely when they go out in the car because that's an obvious safety measure easily achieved, but it's all too easy not to be so careful on the home front, where safety has to be more of a way of thinking and a way of life than a list of such obvious measures. Maybe this goes some of the way to explain the fact that home accidents cause twice as many injuries requiring in-patient hospital treatment than road accidents, where children are concerned.

DON'T GO TOO FAR

Briefly, to go back over some old ground, it's not a case of being over-protective and restricting your child at a time when she should naturally be developing. This will not help you and it would not have helped the mother we mentioned at the beginning of this chapter. There will always be occasions when your child will have to show the ability to think independently for his or her own survival. So wrapping children in cotton wool may keep them safe and sound while you are in control of the situation, but if anything goes wrong with the perfect environment you have created, the soft, woolly protection will not go far.

In addition, the image created of the over-protective parent is that of someone who cannot relax enough to enjoy her children and who is too busy worrying to get on with her own life. Instead, looking after the children and protecting them from anything and everything has completely taken over.

If you take a different attitude and if you manage to create an environment that you are satisfied is a safe one, you will be able to relax and enjoy your children. One way of making sure the environment is safe is trying to see it from where your child is standing – literally. Get down on your hands and knees and view the world from down below. See how vulnerable you feel if you're near a door which could swing open at any moment. The door could then jolt against your body and if there's an unsuspecting 'big person' walking through holding a mug of tea that's a double danger to contend with. A mug full of tea spilt over a child is the equivalent to a bucketful spilt over an adult because of the difference in size.

When you play with your children – and be careful to join in at their level, not to take over and control what's going on – you can learn a great deal about what they're capable of and how they think. By being perceptive you'll be able to notice how well they can use their hands, how far they can climb, how strong they are, how well they can balance. All these factors must be taken into account when you're making your home safe. But we cannot repeat often enough how important it is to be one step ahead.

Question: Is there a lock on your chest freezer? If not, get one: the first you may know of the way your son or daughter is capable of opening the top and climbing in is when the deed is done. Then safety precautions of any nature may well be too late.

STAIRS

Every year too many children between 1 and 4 years old die after falling down the stairs. Take care that no toys, shoes, or anything else, are left on any staircase or near the top of one. Take care when you are carrying a child – the heavier the child is the more likely you are to trip or fall, especially if she isn't keen on the journey upwards or downwards and is indicating that rather physically with her legs and arms. And be careful of anything that might encourage your child to come down the stairs more quickly than she should, such as shouting up to her the arrival of a favourite aunt, playmate, or pudding!

ACCIDENTAL POISONING

The most common age for accidental poisoning is 2 years old and generally it's a risk for all children in their pre-school years.

> In one recent year nearly 9,000 3- and 4-year-olds were poisoned at home.

Child-resistant containers for pills, medicine, or cleaning materials are good ideas, but child-resistant does not mean child-proof. Children as young as 2 have managed to open them. It is better not to take any risks and to keep all of the poisonous substances we've listed at the back of the book, and any others you can think of in your home, well out of reach. The average home has dozens and dozens of poisonous substances which is an awful lot of poison. Add to this fact the way that modern homes tend to be built with less and less storage space and it seems a lot of DIY may be on the cards – putting up high shelves and locked cupboards, and making drawers and other cupboards child-resistant. It's a large amount of work which will no doubt have to be carried out on a day you'd rather be taking it easy, but it has to be worth it.

One whole area of poisonous substances it's impossible to lock away or place on high shelving is plants and berries. There's an added disadvantage here in that parents themselves may not be able to distinguish between what can be safely eaten and what can't. At the back of this book we list useful organisations, some of which can give you information about this problem. But as a general rule we'd suggest that you didn't pick mushrooms, blackberries, bilberries or any other wild fruit or vegetable with your 2 to 5-year-old in tow or joining in. Even if you are confident that you can tell the difference between an edible mushroom and a poisonous toadstool, a cherry and a deadly nightshade berry, there are too many harmful plants and berries which look like those which are perfectly safe, and this can confuse a young child who can make mistakes. In any case it encourages them to pick and eat what they find in the garden, the park or the countryside, whatever it looks like. And that can be very, very hazardous.

DID YOU KNOW?

Interestingly, the seeds of some everyday fruits can be poisonous. This list includes apples, cherries, peaches, and plums. If the stones and pips are chewed cyanide can be released. But the occasional chewed stone or swallowed pip won't do any harm. Castor oil seeds and rosary pea seeds are also dangerous, although these are rare in Britain. The leaves of the rhubarb plant have been known to kill if they're eaten and, apart from the tomato and potato, all others parts of the tomato plant and potato plant are poisonous. Many flowers are poisonous and so are bulbs, so don't allow your child to eat either.

Signs of poisoning

Confusion, stomach pains, vomiting, skin burns, unconsciousness, and staining of the skin around the mouth. If your child exhibits any of these signs, she might have eaten or drunk something poisonous.

Gardens generally can contain hazards, from hosepipes to trip over, rakes to step on, and all sorts of sharp tools and poisonous chemicals. Make sure anything dangerous is locked in the garden shed or the garage. Take care when using any of these things when children are about.

INHALATION

Some substances found in the home and in the garden shed which are poisonous can also be inhaled and this can be just as dangerous. The average home has around thirty products which can be abused in this way from glue, to antifreeze, aerosols, paint thinner, nail varnish, nail varnish remover and butane gas. If an abuser becomes seriously intoxicated he or she can become completely unaware of everyday hazards and so be at great risk of accidents. This may seen to be a very early time to be worrying about this sort of danger and it's true that most abusers are older, but cases of children as young as 4 and 5 sniffing these substances have been known.

BURNS

Burning is still a danger. One 3-year-old opened an oven door and climbed on to it. The cooker tipped and a pan of boiling food poured over the toddler who suffered 20% burns – that means 20% of his body was burned. Other small children have been badly burned climbing into baths which parents have run for themselves and which are therefore at a far hotter temperature than they would run for a child. As we said, it's a good idea when there are small children in the house to keep your hot water thermostat down to below 54° centigrade, 130° Fahrenheit, and not to run very hot baths for anyone. They're not especially good for you anyway. Don't let your child walk downstairs holding anything hot like a hot water bottle (or anything sharp or glass for that matter). If she trips and lands on whatever she was holding she could be badly hurt. Hot water bottles can burst, glass can shatter. Also beware that burning and poisoning can combine if a toddler lays her hands on sterilising tablets which are meant for a small baby's equipment and manages to swallow them. So if you have a small child and a baby to care for at the same time, you'll need to watch out for that.

STRANGULATION

Strangulation is also a problem. Take care that apparatus including bunkbeds do not have gaps in the structure, between the safety rail and mattress or the ladder for example, which would trap a child by the neck if she slipped and fell. There have also been recent reports of youngsters playing with curtain cords and strangling themselves by accident.

SUFFOCATION AND CHOKING

- Children occasionally suffocate after inhaling pen caps. Look for felt tips and ball points with new, safer, ventilated caps.

- This is also the age when it's seen as a great game to pretend to be spacemen by putting plastic bags over heads. *Don't let them*, even if there are holes in the plastic. There may not be holes in the next one they find.

- Youngsters this age can still choke. It's best not to give them grapes, nuts, especially peanuts, or hard sweets until they're 4 or older.

LOOKING GOOD

If your child needs glasses, ask your optician about plastic or splinter-proof lenses. While we were writing this book, someone mentioned to us that when she was a youngster, her dad accidentally hit her in the eye with a cricket bat during a family game. The glasses she was wearing had toughened glass, so although the lens shattered, none left the frame, and none went in her eye.

WHEN THE CAT'S AWAY....

Because your child is growing up, the games she'll be playing and how she wants to spend her time will be changing all the time. But she'll still need more or less constant supervision. It's amazing the number of accidents that happen while mum is answering the door and, to an even greater degree, the number that happen while she is on the phone. It's always worth glancing round the corner to check everything's alright. Silence may seem to be golden to the busy dad with a migraine or the busy mum with period pains, but it's not. In reality silences can spell danger. We've heard of one mother who realised she hadn't heard from her son for around five minutes. She went upstairs to look for him and spotted only his fingertips: he was hanging out of the bathroom window. She rushed to save him – and stopped a terrible disaster in the process (a story which reminds us again of the need for window locks or safety catches).

Keep in communication with your children even if you're not in the same room as them. The level of supervision still needs to be very high. You may, for instance, have a serving hatch you can look through to see what they're getting up to.

TOYS AND GAMES

Don't over-estimate the interest they'll have in television at this age. Of course all that colour and movement will be attractive but young children have only a short interest span. That's why cartoons are the most popular programmes for them. Other programmes may not hold their attention and they could get up to all sorts of dangerous mischief while your assuming they're sitting quietly in front of the box.

Once *Tom and Jerry* is over, they'll be moving their attention towards new toys which require their own safety rules – tricycles, bicycles, and pedal cars, for a start. It's hard to think of a piece of equipment that spells out in more obvious terms the need for safety glass or film over glass doors and low windows and the continuing need for gates at the top of stairs, and at the front door or the end of the front garden.

Your child's day-to-day life may include other great games which could become dangerous if they're not seen from the safety point of view. All children enjoy dressing up in grown ups' clothes but they could fall badly if they're stomping around in mum's high heels. And they can just as easily choke on a loose button from your old posh frock as they can on one from their own clothes. Cut off anything that might be dangerous.

Children of 3 and 4 will be starting to use glue, scissors, and crayons as they create their early masterpieces. Teach your safety lessons early on and prevent needless screams and screeches. Make sure, for instance, that they only use round-ended scissors.

A great game will continue to be copying what mum and dad and older brothers and sisters do. This is a good time to mention smoking again. Research has shown us that children are aware of cigarettes even before they reach the age of 5 if they see people smoking around them. A mother smoking is more likely to influence her child than a father smoking because traditionally she'll be with her for longer periods. Not only will your child be a victim of passive smoking, but she is also more likely to be a smoker when she grows up.

Did you know?

In a house where both parents smoke a child inhales an average of the equivalent of 80 cigarettes a year, and is more likely to suffer chest infections and other respiratory diseases in the long run as a result.

It's also important that you don't take pills in front of your child, and keep razors, kettles, irons, toys only meant for older children, and any other potential hazards out of reach.

Another 'great game' children will discover is finding out how things work – electric sockets, for example. You must tell your child 'No' if there's any sign of her going anywhere near one. Dummy plugs which cover the sockets are a good idea as long as they're not the brightly decorated ones which might attract a child.

REMEMBER, REMEMBER....

While we're on the subject of brightly coloured attractions, our advice on the firework front is only to attend properly and expertly organised public displays. Do not attempt to look after children, fireworks, bonfire, baked potatoes, anguished pets, and duff sparklers which won't sparkle, in the back yard, single- (or double-) handedly.

HOME FROM HOME

It's likely that as your child gets older she will be spending more and more time away from your own home. If you're a working mum this will already be the case. And it's even more important, when you will not be around to watch over your child, that you're satisfied with all safety precautions that the person minding your child has taken. So if there's anything worrying you it's worth mentioning it to her (or him). If you think the corners on the coffee table look too sharp and could hurt a toddler running into them, say something. It doesn't have to sound as if you're trying to take over or as if you know better, just a gentle suggestion and a 'don't you think' question is all that's needed.

The same is also true of grandparents looking after their

grandchildren. It can feel awkward for you to intervene and tell them what to do. After all, for most of your life they'll have been telling you what to do. But they will have forgotten some of the safety precautions they used to take when you were small. On top of this there are all sorts of appliances and gadgets about now that weren't about then – microwave cookers, for example. They'll need to be told not to heat a small child's food up in a microwave unless they're extremely careful. This is because the food can get alarmingly hot in the middle area even if it appears cooler on the outside. Children can get burnt.

OFF TO THE PLAYGROUND

> **Did you know?**
>
> Each year, around 150,000 injuries result from playground accidents.
>
> 4 out of every 5 of these accidents occurred *even though the children were being supervised*.

This is a big new danger area for children when they reach the 2 to 5 age group, unless you know which hazards to look out for. Even quiet, shy children can become more reckless when they're with others of the same age, so be sure to keep an eye on all of them. They'll still be overcoming the problems of balance and might start to get over-confident when they see other children climbing about with ease. So remember:

- Don't send your toddlers to the playground – or the swimming pool for that matter – with your older children. It's so easy for even responsible children to be distracted by the thrills and spills – though hopefully there won't be too many spills. So it's not fair on either the older or the younger child. It's easy enough for parents to be distracted by the other parents who'll no doubt be there to talk to. Older children may not be patient enough with their young brothers and sisters and may expect them to be capable of holding on tight to a roundabout or climbing frame when it's all really a bit too much for them.

- Look carefully at your local playground before deciding it's safe. Playgrounds need soft ground or grass, not tarmac or concrete which don't do anything, or certainly not enough, to soften the impact of a fall. Very serious injuries can be caused from a fall of just 1 foot if a child is unlucky. In fact 75% of playground accidents involve falls onto hard surfaces. Look for playgrounds with a rubberised floor.

- Make sure the equipment looks secure and maintained. Too often it's not. You should report any lapses in safety standards, including broken glass on the ground, to the local council in charge of upkeep.

- There should be plenty of space around the swings so no one walking past is in any danger of being hit by flying legs – a moving swing can reach speeds of *up to 25 miles per hour*. Being hit with a seat edge at that speed is said to be the equivalent of a child being hit with the force of a 5-ton truck. Broken necks and fractured skulls and backbones have resulted from this sort of accident. Seats should be made of rubber or plastic, not wood. Those made of tyres are the softest, biggest, and safest. One survey has revealed that although boys have more accidents with slides, roundabouts and climbing frames, girls have the same number of accidents involving swings as boys do.

- If other children are misbehaving it's always worth pointing this out in a disapproving way. It's better to tell your child that 'Those boys standing up and kneeling on the swings are being naughty', than to leave her to copy them.

- Don't encourage your child to go higher than she feels she can cope with on a climbing frame or to try the biggest slide when she only wants to use the small one. If she feels frightened she will be tense, and tension causes accidents. Falling from the top of a high climbing frame can be equivalent to falling from a first floor window – and just think how we'd feel if we saw our children about to do that. So don't let misplaced parental pride ('Look at my little Katie, isn't she clever') get in the way of your sense of what is safe and what isn't. Unfortunately there isn't a great deal of labelling of playground equipment to tell you what age groups it's suitable for. There also isn't the same sort of supervision that we find in swimming pools. These are two issues it's worth campaigning about but in the meantime you'll have to be the judge – or your child may be able to judge for herself.

- Make sure your child's footwear is suitable. The wellies that are great for slushing along through piles of fallen leaves may not be so great for clambering up and down metal frames. Make sure clothing is suitable too. Super-hero style cloaks, for example, could be dangerous wear for climbing frames.

- The safest slides by far are those built into hills or slopes, not those which are free standing. Also worth avoiding are the long, plank swings which seat three or more children at a time, witches hats – octagonal swings which go round and round – and the rocking horses on which children sit in a line (these have been banned but some may still be around).

- Teach your child the safe way to jump off roundabouts and how to use swings so they won't get hurt, when you feel they're old enough. But note that the accident rate for boys, according to one survey, peaks at 5 years old, and then again at 10, while for girls it peaks at 9. Very young boys are obviously at risk. Tell them not to panic. If they ever feel nervous on a piece of equipment, when they realise how high up they are, for example, they mustn't fret, they must keep still and call you.

SWIMMING POOLS

When it comes to swimming pools, unless your youngster is a very good swimmer – and we'd recommend that children learn to swim at as young an age as possible – make sure she's wearing arm bands or other inflatable protection, but don't take it for granted that makes her safe. Rubber rings have been known to keep children upside down in the water fighting for air rather than the right way up. Keep with her. Remember that swimming in a heated pool is quite different from a cold canal or river. Don't let youngsters swim in these settings. Never rely on older children to care for toddlers in a swimming pool. No child under 8 should swim without an adult.

There'll always be tumbles in playgrounds, in swimming pools and in all places where children play. Tumbles are one thing, serious accidents are quite another.

ON THE ROAD

This is another area to focus on. And for this age group you need to approach it from several different angles: for your child as pedestrian, as passenger... and as football-chaser! In one set of recent annual figures, 57 under-5s who were pedestrians were killed (this figure will include the football players) and 44 car passenger under-5s were killed in road accidents. This second figure was by far the highest for any of the age groups covering children. There were also a startling 3 child deaths among pedal cyclists under 5. It should go without saying that young children should not be allowed to cycle or play in any form on roads no matter how quiet they are and how well behaved the children. That goes for quiet cul-de-sacs as well as busier roads.

No child of 5 or under should be anywhere near a road without you being present. She will rely on you for guidance on how to cross a road, which is a frightening proposition for a youngster. As the mother mentioned at the beginning of this chapter showed, it is possible for a parent to make a mistake, and this can have devastating consequences. We can only recommend that you as parents admit to your children when you feel you've slipped up (and not just where safety is concerned) so your child will realise that sometimes mummy makes a mistake. And if you drum home the road safety message on top of that – explaining to a toddler *why* you're crossing the road at a particular time, place and pace, and getting her to join in the constant check for cars, looking and listening as you both cross – as well as saving your 'No' booming voice for occasions such as this, you can then only hope for the best. You'll have done all you can.

Remember:

- Keep a tight grip on young hands when you're walking anywhere near a road. We've heard one horrifying tale of a parent whose grip must have loosened momentarily. The child slipped away, into the road and straight under a car. Walking reins might still be a good idea.

- Make sure your garden, yard, or drive is securely fenced in. Ask yourself if you need a gate behind the front door to stop a very active child running out after a toy or pet.

IN THE CAR

- Unload your car before unstrapping your child and lifting or letting her out of the passenger side. Otherwise you might be too preoccupied with your shopping bags to notice where she's running off to – and it could be into the road. Child deaths in road accidents increase from around four a year for the under 1s to nearly 100 a year for the 1 to 4s. It's no coincidence that children are mobile throughout their time in the second age group but only for a few months of the first.

- Have child locks fitted for children aged round 3 and older.

- Never let your child stand or sit without any appropriate safety belt or seat in the front of the car and never let your child stand in the back seat. Child car seats, properly anchored to one of the fixed car seats or strapped to it with an adult seat belt, really are seen as a must these days for children under 5. Make sure that you fasten them properly. A good one will have additional harness slots so that as your child grows she will still be able to use the seat. If the child car seat has a tray, don't allow your children to use pencils or pens or anything else inside the car which could cause injury if the car stops suddenly.

- If your child is travelling in a friend's or a relative's car which does not have a child car seat, the best idea is for her to be strapped in with an adult seatbelt in the back seat, ideally with a booster cushion specially designed for the purpose; if this is impossible, the next solution is for her to be strapped in the front seat; the least advisable is that she be unrestrained in the back. Of course the seatbelt should be adjusted so that it is not too big for your child – it should not be slack and should run smoothly across the rib cage and shoulder. The strap which crosses the lap should cross the top of the thighs, not the tummy.

- A child should never ride in the boot area of a hatchback car.

- If there aren't enough seat belts to go round, strap in the heaviest people – the adults. In a crash the unrestrained people will be like missiles in the car and it's better to have small, light missiles than big, heavy ones.

- Make sure your children are on their best behaviour when they're in the car. They may need telling quite firmly that mum or dad who's usually such fun can't join in the jollity when they're behind the steering wheel.

TRAINS AND BUSES

When using trains and buses, take care to hold on tightly to your youngsters when getting on and off. With trains and tube trains, remember to 'mind the gap' – small children will not be able to judge it as well as you can.

Did you know?

Escalators can be dangerous, too! The most vulnerable people injured on escalators are the over-65s and the under-5s - and particularly 3-year-olds. Watch that clothing doesn't get caught in the escalator. Careful parental supervision of children on escalators is very important.

GETTING LOST

This is a frightening proposition for any child. All under-5s depend so heavily on their parents for their security and all of a sudden that security has disappeared. So:

- Teach your child her name, address, and phone number as soon as she's able to remember it.

- Teach her from a very young age not to do what any stranger says, talk to any stranger, or take anything from a stranger, but always to ask mum first, or whoever's in charge of her.

- Explain that if she ever gets lost in a shop she should stay in the shop on the floor she's on, and wait for mum to find her – she shouldn't go looking for mum herself.

- Teach her to go to somebody else's mum for help, or to a man in uniform or person behind a counter.

- Tell her where she is going and who is in charge of her if it isn't you.

There really shouldn't be any reason for your child to get lost except for being accidentally separated from you in a crowd. Children of 5 years old and younger are far too young to go anywhere by themselves and your home should be secure enough to prevent them wandering off.

BULLYING

You must not allow your child to be bullied either by a parent, by another adult or by other children. If you know of an adult bullying your child you must step in to stop it, seeking help if necessary. Your first loyalty must be to your child. No matter what she has done she will not deserve a beating. If she is misbehaving it's likely to be a result of her insecurity and if she has a parent or 'carer' who is willing or has the capacity to beat her, it is no wonder she feels insecure.

If she is being threatened by another child, tell her there is more safety in numbers and to get help. It is not sneaky to tell the teacher at play school or nursery school. Otherwise a group of other children should scare the bully off. Tell your child if the bully wants something she has, it is more important that she keeps herself safe than that she holds on to whatever it is the bully wants so badly. At this age this is probably only likely if she gets separated from you accidentally and is approached by older children in the street or another public place.

SEXUAL ABUSE

Your very young child should not be coming into contact with strangers, and this means if your child is at risk from a child abuser it's most likely to be someone who is known to you. Indeed, the facts show the abuser is usually a man, and a near relative, close friend, husband or live-in-lover of the mother – even her physically mature son. You will of course have absolutely no idea of that person's intentions but it's as well to think of the possibility.

- A child abuser can be someone who appears on the surface to be an extremely doting, caring, attentive uncle. We're not saying you should suspect all adults – we're simply saying you should not dismiss any signs of abuse your child may show and the direction the evidence points in, because it seems to be unthinkable.

- Babysitters can be another source of danger. They could have been victims of abuse themselves and have manoeuvred themselves into a job which will give them the opportunity to repeat the abuse on others. They could be teenagers who've reached puberty and want to experiment. Never put children in charge of children. You may be cutting costs by employing schoolchildren but it is far better to pay a responsible adult the going rate and have peace of mind.

- Remember, boys and girls are equally vulnerable to child abuse. In 95% of reported cases abusers are male, which means that *5% are female* – a thought that's somehow more difficult to understand.

- Children rarely lie about sexual abuse – unless they're saying they haven't been assaulted when really they have.

The child help organisation Kidscape has issued the following lists of signs which might help you recognise that something is wrong, whether or not that something is sexual abuse. You should be especially concerned if several of these are relevant to your child or if one is relevant to a great degree:

- Changing personality, such as becoming insecure or clingy.

- Regressing to younger behaviour patterns, such as thumb sucking or bringing out discarded cuddly toys.

- Suddenly losing appetite or eating compulsively.

- Becoming isolated or withdrawn.

- Being unable to concentrate.

- Lacking trust in a familiar adult, such as not wanting to be alone with a babysitter or childminder.

- Starting to wet themselves again, day or night.

- Having nightmares, being unable to sleep.

- Being overly affectionate and knowledgeable in a sexual way inappropriate to the child's age.

- Having medical problems such as chronic itching or a pain in the genitals.

If your child needs help, contact the National Society for the Prevention of Cruelty to Children or your local social services department, unless you are in Scotland; in which case contact the Royal Scottish Society for the Prevention of Cruelty to Children or the local Social Work Department. If you prefer you can call the Police, or tell your doctor or health visitor, or the child's teacher, or call a voluntary organisation which deals with child sexual abuse.

Remember, your first loyalty and your first priority must be to your child. A child of this age can never be anything other than an innocent victim – and you may be her only hope.

Chapter Five
COMMUNICATING WITH YOUR 2-5 YEAR OLD

We've all had that feeling. We're absolutely shattered. A marathon runner wilting in the heat of the sun has more energy in his big toe than we can muster in our whole bodies. We feel it's all we can do to get the kids fed, cleaned, and quietened down for bed. And even that seems to be more than we can realistically be expected to manage.

But most of the time we should all accept that what we invest in our children has got to be just that – our time, and a fair proportion of our energy. Giving them a healthy meal three times a day and making sure they get a good night's sleep and the occasional blast of exercise isn't all it takes for them to grow into healthy adults. We wouldn't be happy if we were eating a wonderful meal in a lovely restaurant but the rest of the customers were all being rude to us and turning their noses up at our table manners – we might feel full up if we managed to scrape our plates clean, but we certainly wouldn't feel satisfied and ready to face the world (although it's more likely that however good the meal looked we wouldn't be able to face it). In the same way children need care and love along with their fish fingers and chocolate pudding rather than constant criticism and coldness. Some children lose weight during stressful times in their families which shows that care and love is important for their physical as well as their emotional growth.

In fact this is especially true for pre-school children who are in what psychologists call their 'formative years'. These are the years which will play a large part in establishing how secure and balanced they will be as they get older. With time and care you can teach emotions as well as learn them and these are the important years for children learning how to deal with their emotions. The lessons they learn during this early time in their lives will not be easily forgotten. That's why communicating properly with them at this age and developing your relationship with them is so important.

Of course you'll occasionally feel like dumping them on a different planet – or dumping yourself on a desert island to do nothing except drink coconut milk. For those parents bringing up one child or more single-handedly or with a partner who is rarely or never supportive and doesn't lend a hand this is, of course, even more true. But investing time and energy now will be worthwhile. It is an investment which will bring dividends. Some of these will be immediate but others will affect their future safety – and your future peace of mind.

YOU'RE STILL IN CHARGE

One message that you should continue to deliver to your children is that you are still very much in charge. You know about life, its good side, its bad side, and its dangers; your toddler doesn't. But as we've said before, that doesn't mean you should be dictatorial in your tone. You shouldn't be saying, 'I'm the boss around here' when you ask them to do something, but you should spell out that because you care, you need to take control of some aspects of their life.

LET THEM HAVE THEIR SAY

Anything to do with safety is non-negotiable, from using the child safety seat in the car to holding their hands when walking along the street. But of course you can negotiate on other matters. Allow your child to choose what colour socks she wants to wear or which of two jumpers she'd like to put on. This will help her see that you are willing to listen to her wishes and it will teach her a very early lesson in making decisions.

A UNITED FRONT

It's worth re-emphasising at this stage how important it is that parents are consistent about their safety messages and supportive of each other. Never argue about safety messages in front of the children, although this is difficult to achieve. Discuss the whole question of safety between yourselves. If dad doesn't spend as much time with the children as mum he might not be as aware of the stage of their development and understanding. The main carer must try to explain this fully. So if dad wants to leave his sharp-edged garden tools out while he stops for a cup of tea and says the children should simply be instructed to leave them well alone, but mum's of the firm opinion that they should be put away for safety's sake, she should explain to him why this is. We would agree with mum – children in this age group will love to copy what they see mum and dad doing and it might be hard to issue an instruction which will stop them having a go at 'gardening like dad' if your attention wanders. But we would disagree with both parents if they argued about this in front of the children. The children must receive a uniform message which will help them learn there are no two sides to the safety debate where they are concerned.

If mum tells her little boy off for jumping off the sofa but daddy is delighted at his son's antics and applauds him with a 'Who's a brave boy then' and a paternal slap on the back, not only will the child be confused about which message to believe, it will give him too much power in the family. He will be able to play one parent off against the other and it will be much harder to discipline him on health and safety matters. For parents to vie for the affections of their child – for dad to paint himself as the good guy who comes in in the evenings and gives his boy sweets and hugs but who doesn't want to disturb the great relationship between himself and 'Dad's little lad' by reinforcing his wife's instructions if his son's been very naughty – is very damaging.

It's much more difficult to develop a uniform approach if your relationship as a couple isn't going well. If you're arguing between yourselves or even deciding to separate or divorce, you must both agree not to use your children as weapons in your battles. In these situations the chance of maintaining co-operation between both parents is jeopardised. There are a whole new set of reasons not to agree or not to be seen to agree with your partner. But you must remember that the battle is between the two of you – your children should not be involved in that. Even though you may be determined not to agree in many areas, you should agree on any area to do with the children. Just because you're getting on terribly it doesn't mean you have to be terrible parents. Sit down and thrash out a policy and back each other up on it.

This is important because children develop a sense of guilt at a surprisingly young age. They value your approval and are upset by your disapproval. They thrive on your encouragement and praise. But if your children know that if they gain disapproval from one parent for misbehaving they can simply turn to another for affection, they will be less likely to respect instructions when it really matters – when they're about to run into the road or stick a knitting needle into an electric socket.

BE REALISTIC

It's also true that if you set your standards too high and if nothing your children do is ever quite right and they never gain your encouragement and praise they may become disobedient and difficult. To their young eyes and minds, they'll have nothing to gain from being obedient and well-behaved. And the same is true if you are not giving your children the attention they need. Another result of this might be that your child becomes more accident-prone as she is not being properly controlled and has no authority figure to look up to who will guide her behaviour.

This is a time when it is important gently to encourage your child's independence. But it must be done gently – don't force her to do things she doesn't want to which jeopardise her safety, such as crossing quiet roads by herself. She's simply not old enough. Don't force her to slide down a big slide in a playground. If she doesn't want to she'll be tense and worried and that's when accidents are likely. Let her develop her own sense of judgement. Ask her if she wants to go on the big slide. When she's ready she'll say yes, and even then she may want you to hold her hand on the way down. That's not being over-protective. It's allowing your child to develop at a speed that's right for her.

There are other, more subtle, ways by which you can encourage your young child's independence. Allow her to help with housework so long as there's nothing dangerous involved. Allow her to dawdle home from the shops with you, inspecting anything interesting she passes. If she doesn't want you to cuddle her, then don't – respect her feelings in that way. If she wants to wear a particular outfit and it's suitable, let her. Ask her opinion.

This isn't spoiling her, it's helping her to develop her own mind. Apart from those accidents caused by faulty goods, most others can be avoided if one simple rule is followed. 'Think before you act.' If we train our youngsters to think for themselves we'll be helping them do just that.

FINDING THE RIGHT LEVEL

When you are investing your time and energy talking to your child, it's important to make sure you are communicating on her level. Play very safe with safety issues. Use very simple language. Don't speak at the top level of her understanding, pitch safety instructions well within your child's grasp. They'll need repeating more than once. Use a simple language structure with no double negatives or any other complicated phrases, and use simple vocabulary. Some adults find it easy to adapt their language and their actions to that of their child. It comes naturally and intuitively to them. For others it isn't that easy. It's certainly true that all children will have different levels of understanding. Some will be able to comprehend relatively complex concepts quite early, others won't. With many children what they can understand can be directly related to their level of speech – as they speak more you know they can understand more and you can pitch your chats with them by bearing in mind their own speaking ability. But we know of more than one child who has been quite backward when it comes to speaking but who has understood what she's been told perfectly well. Their minds have been too busy concentrating on other things around them to concentrate on speaking. Their speech then developed perfectly normally, although later than average.

So it is important not to underestimate what your child can understand. But it's also vital you don't over-estimate. This is a much more widespread failing. Many parents tend to give their young children warnings in broadly adult terms but children can't understand this properly. They will be confused and even though they might grasp the instruction you're giving them they may not understand *why* you're giving it. The message will therefore be a less powerful one.

SAY WHAT YOU MEAN

This means if you're warning your youngster not to talk to strangers, you shouldn't say, 'Don't speak to strangers – it might lead to problems.' A child won't be able to relate to the vague concept of 'lead to problems'. If a parent speaks in those vague terms about a subject as important as this it may be that he or she feels embarrassed about it, or scared of what the child might ask next. Mum or dad might feel unsure about what to say about possible sexual abuse to a child so young. The answer is that you might not have to, yet. Just think how much more it would mean to a child if you simply said, 'Don't speak to strangers – they might hurt you.' There isn't a child anywhere in the world who doesn't understand the concept of hurting.

If you just say, 'It's not nice to hit another child,' it's possible your child won't fully understand the concept of being 'nice' to others and so will not fully understand your message. Far better to add, 'Don't hit him because he'll hit you back and he might not ask you to his birthday party.'

And don't say, 'Be careful of cars – they are dangerous things.' It's far better to say, 'Be careful of cars – if you ran in front of one you could get hurt. You might break your leg.' So communicating a message in terms a child can understand is more of an art than some people may imagine. It doesn't come naturally to everyone, although the more relaxed you are with your child and the more you understand her, the easier it should be.

DON'T GO TOO FAR

But be careful not to be unnecessarily frightening. Don't suggest to your pre-schooler that if she does something she'll damage you or her other parent, or she will lose one of you or both of you in some way, or she will be taken away from you. For instance, don't say, 'Be careful of cars because if one comes and runs you over you'll be taken away to hospital and we won't be able to see you for months.' Don't say, 'If you play with that knife you will cut yourself and you will have to go to hospital and you will never be able to draw again.' If your message is so scary as to suggest that she will be separated from you, her family, or her home, or that she will be totally abandoned in some strange place, you will undermine your child's sense of security and confidence. Get your message across without scaring the wits out of her.

There's another reason for not saying, 'You will never be able to draw again.' when you're trying to stop her playing with a knife you've left out during a lapse in concentration. If she carries on and cuts herself and the cut really isn't that bad, she'll soon find she's perfectly capable of using a pencil or crayon again. If you'd just said, 'If you cut yourself it will hurt you', she would see that you were right. But if you'd exaggerated she'd have seen that you weren't right – even that you'd lied, however well-meaning your warning had been. It is never a good idea to lie in front of your children. It's not an example you want them to copy.

Another way of scaring your child which is also a bad idea but which is less easy to control from your point of view, happens because you are very worried about her. If, say, you think she's taken some pills or something else which might be poisonous, it's very important that you keep calm about it. If you're not and you start shouting or even shaking her, she might think you are very angry and she'll be punished if she tells you the truth. Every child will lie if the situation is threatening enough and in this case, if you seem to be threatening her, her lies might cause a great deal of pain and harm.

Another common error is to confuse your children with the messages you're giving out – and this can happen even if you and your partner have agreed on all safety issues and all discipline issues. If your child hits you or another child and you tell her it's bad to hit but then you smack her, it can be very confusing for her even at this age.

ALTERNATIVE STRATEGIES

For another reason, too, it's best not to counter aggression with aggression. It might work in the short term – after all, no child likes to be hit – but in the long term it will make your child more aggressive. It might be better to limit her television or cut out her sweet allowance for one day or take away a toy she's been misusing. Constant smacking reduces a child's feelings of guilt about doing something. It can give her a sullen self-righteousness. She may begin to feel she has been wronged. It will make her less inclined to confide in you and will make her more secretive. And she will lie more to avoid punishment. This is not how you want your child to develop.

But it's a difficult dilemma to resolve. If your child isn't disciplined she'll continue behaving badly; if she's disciplined too much she'll become alienated and will lie more. The best thing to do is to try to strike a balance (no pun intended). Make sure when you tell her off you do it in terms she can understand – or she won't understand why what she's doing is wrong and as soon as you've moved away she may carry on misbehaving. And remember that punishment is most effective when it is balanced against the seriousness of the crime. Just as you should only use the warning shout 'No' for safety issues, so you should use the strictest discipline only for the most important misdemeanours. Try to see how bad the underlying motive for your child's bad behaviour is rather than the consequence of her actions. This means that dropping her dinner by accident is far less serious than throwing it on the floor on purpose, although the physical result for you is the same – having to clear it up.

EXPLAIN YOURSELF

It's also important for you to get across to your child that you may not like what she's done when she misbehaves but you still love her. There can hardly be a parent who hasn't smacked a child at some point. And the hurt of a smack is much more than physical hurt – it's knowing that she's lost the approval of the person who matters to her most. You need to reassure her when the argument and the bad feeling is over. You could apologise for losing your temper but explain why she made you upset and angry. Always make sure your child knows why she did wrong and why you were cross. If you just shout and give her a whack she might just start up again as soon as you're no longer in sight.

ADMITTING YOU'RE WRONG

Apologising for your actions is especially important if you hit out in relief. For example you may have scooped your child out of the path of cars on a busy road. It may have been your fault that she got there in the first place – maybe your attention had drifted to counting how much cash you had left in your purse, but it's still quite a common reaction to smack because of the sudden tension and worry her actions will have caused. Explain why you did it, give her a cuddle. Say, 'Mummy was tired,' or 'Mummy was worried,' so she doesn't think she's been bad.

In fact it isn't a good idea in general to pretend you're always in the right. The world outside isn't perfect – your children will find that out for themselves soon enough – and so maybe it's more real for you to admit your mistakes. If you slip up on the safety rules you insist on so stringently for your children, admit it, and apologise. How many parents haven't heard, 'Mummy, mummy, the green man wasn't there' when they've crossed the road a split second before the lights have changed at a pelican crossing? Acknowledge that your little critic is absolutely right and that, yes, mum was wrong. If instead you tell her to 'Shut up, be quiet and get a move on,' how can you expect her to keep to your safety standards? You're not keeping to them yourself. You've caused more confusion, more resentment, and a feeling of injustice in a young mind which should instead be preoccupied with pride for remembering mum's road safety message. And knowing mum can make mistakes may be one way of getting that message across to the youngster we've already mentioned, whose mum crossed the road and who obediently and unthinkingly followed her into the path of a car. If she had had that reason to pause and think it would have given her mother added vital moments to yell 'No' and her instructions.

LEARNING RESPONSIBILITY

Important research has been carried out by the Primary School Project funded by the Health Education Authority at the University of Southampton's Health Education Department. There researchers have analysed the views of more than 2,000 children on safety and whose responsibility it is to keep them safe, expressed through drawings and writing. The results show overwhelmingly that for children aged 4 to 8, there's a universal belief that it is a job for mum and dad, or for other adults – policemen, teachers, and others in authority. And even among 9-year-olds only one in four mention themselves when asked whose responsibility it is to keep them safe wherever they are. But children can be taught to start to take care of themselves as early as 2 or 3 years old. They can start to see that it's partly their responsibility at a very early age if you are willing to teach them.

Teaching them this is a complex business. We've already pointed out that thinking about safety should be your sixth sense when you've got a baby or a young child in the home, but communicating to them efficiently that this is their business, too, is something else. It combines the skills of politician, diplomat, teacher, friend, and playmate.

KEEP IT SIMPLE

Again, it's important to use simple language and concepts they understand. Don't worry about using short sentences – it's more important that what you're telling them flows logically. You could try to make it flow in the correct order of events as well by saying, 'If you play with that knife you might cut yourself and hurt yourself,' rather than, 'You will hurt yourself if you play with that knife.' But what's more important is that you stress the important words, not being afraid to use facial expression and actions. Don't mumble a message out of a sense of duty to make yourself feel OK. That's *not* OK. Tone of voice is so important when it comes to making a child really listen and not just vaguely hear what you're saying. It's likely that you'll find you have to repeat yourself once or several times.

To make sure your child has understood it's worth getting her to repeat what you've told her. Ask her, 'Why shouldn't you play with the knife?' and hope that she tells you what you've told her. Tell her to explain to her dolls how to keep safe and not hurt themselves while you supervise and check she's got the message. Hopefully this could turn into a game which might be more fun than knife-throwing or sawing the coffee table!

AHA!

Mike, through his years as a broadcaster, has named our next suggestion the 'Aha' technique. Radio and television professionals know that a lot of us keep our sets turned on as background noise – a reassuring patter which we don't really concentrate on. So they find ways to get our attention, they raise points which make us think, 'Aha! That's interesting.'

Your 2 to 5-year-old will no longer be your captive audience. Not everything you do will fascinate her – a lot of it will bore her. But when it comes to safety issues, you want her to think, 'Aha!'.

So if she jumps over a ball in the garden without looking to where she might end up and finds herself in a painful, prickly bush, there'll be tears. But when you comfort her and tell her the hurt will soon be gone and she'll soon be better, why not tell her how for years little children have been told to 'Look before you leap'? Explain to her what the phrase means and get her to tell others around her the lesson she's learned.

Another 'Aha' message which might help to put off toddler tantrums can be repeated when your child is strapped into the car and other members of the family are putting on their own seat belts. Recite to each other the old Jimmy Savile message, 'Clunk, click every trip.' She'll love to be the first to say it.

Children of this age are also receptive to general warnings spoken in a kind, guiding way, not with worry in your voice. 'Do be careful, love,' is one way of encouraging your youngster to take care, be good and make you proud of her.

There's also nothing wrong with old-fashioned, straightforward teaching. If you are looking at berries growing on a bush in the park or in the garden you could use this as an opportunity to put a point across. You could say, 'You can buy berries that are nice to eat and we'll be eating some of them for pudding but there are other berries which are bad for you and make you ill. So you must never pick berries when you are on your own.'

WHAT IF?

The 'What If?' game has been used for decades by parents to communicate with their children and it is still a very efficient and fun way to try to help them keep themselves safe. Remember it is a game – it's not a test with right and wrong answers. It involves parent and child asking each other questions in turn and then talking about the answers they give – or in turn asking a What If? question which leads on from the answer.

So mum might ask, 'What if a man you didn't know came up to you and asked if you'd like a sweet?'. The child might say she wouldn't take it and she'd go and tell you. You could then ask her why. If she isn't clear, you could tell her that the man might look nice but he might be a nasty man who wanted to hurt children. You don't have to add any details which will scare your child and might even give her nightmares. Enough is enough for a child her age.

She, in turn, might use the game to express her worries and ask, 'What would happen if you didn't pick me up from nursery and I was left there all by myself?'. You could then ask her what she'd think she'd do. If she gave the wrong answer – for instance saying she'd try to look for you, you would have to steer her to the right answer – to go and ask her teacher for help. You could say, 'But what if I arrived at the nursery and you weren't there because you'd just left to look for me?'.

'WHEN MUMMY WAS A LITTLE GIRL ...'

Another good way of getting the message across is to tell cautionary tales about what mummy or daddy did when they were small. This fascinates all children – the thought that mummy and daddy might have been as small as they are once upon a time. If you tell them that when you were a little girl or a little boy you hurt yourself very badly when you cut yourself on your daddy's lawnmower after he'd told you not to play with it, and give lots of details about how you felt and what happened to you, the story will interest them and educate them. Next time your child seems to be about to cut herself on something she shouldn't have got hold of, you can remind her of what happened to you; or if she does have an accident, it might be consoling for her to be reminded that you know exactly how she feels. It will also help her to learn that you were forgiven when you were little and that you will forgive her in return.

Explain that accidents and injuries are sometimes the result of what your child does, they're sometimes the result of what someone else does, and they're sometimes no one's fault. Make sure your child doesn't think that she causes all the problems around her. Children do tend to blame themselves for everything from parents separating to milk boiling over. Don't let them.

Other stories that help are those about other people that your child knows. Uncles and aunts and even grandparents are good fodder, for example. It's even more fascinating for youngsters to think of their grandma and grandpa as young children.

This will also have the effect of showing that people in authority and grown-ups, including mum and dad, made mistakes when they were little. It shows that little bits of naughtiness are OK – they're certainly not the end of the world. And stories which illustrate minor misdemeanours can be turned into lessons about real dangers.

TIMES TO TEACH

Even routine chores can turn into lessons in safety once your child reaches that level of understanding. Laying a table can become another way of explaining about the dangers of playing with knives or handling them wrongly. Your child should be made aware of how serious something is by the tone in your voice and how you're telling her. When you're washing up and she's watching, explain how careful you are when you're handling glasses because they could hurt someone if they were broken. If you're out and see some older boys climbing trees or larking about at the top of a climbing frame, explain why you have to be careful when you're so far above the ground. Ask her first to think of how much it hurts if she falls off a chair, and tell her to imagine how much more it would hurt if she fell off something quite so high up.

When you're crossing a road, talk her through it. Don't be sloppy even if there aren't any cars about as far as you can see. Your child will learn from you. Look and listen as you cross and get her to join in. If she spots a car in the distance, then praise her for noticing it – she's getting the idea. Don't just head for a zebra crossing, explain *why* you're going to cross there and tell her to look at the black and white lines. Then maybe find her a picture of a zebra when you get home or on your next trip to a book shop or the library so she can see the black and white lines there too. Your safety message doesn't have to be a formal sit-down chat. It can be part of your developing relationship with your child, part of your day-to-day lives together and part of the way you show her that you care.

DO YOU KNOW WHAT YOUR CHILD IS FRIGHTENED OF?

One of the things you won't get out of a very formal talk with your child is knowledge of what really frightens her – what she thinks she is keeping safe from. The Southampton researchers found out, when they gave children crayons and paper, that the answer to this for 4 and 5-year-olds is very interesting indeed. Imaginary dangers headed the list: aliens, monsters, ghosts, skeletons, werewolves, crocodiles, gorillas, and tigers. Also included in their lists were: burglars, bad men, big boys, 'mum smacking me', cars, cookers, kettles, glass, 'the road', and 'getting lost'.

Once you know what your child *thinks* she has to keep safe from, it makes the whole business of helping her to keep safe that much easier. It will enable you to explain the difference between 'mum smacking me' or 'mum telling me off', which is something you do because you are worried about them and are concerned for them (which in most households does not pose a real threat apart from to their immediate happiness), and those on their lists which are real threats.

RESPECT HER FEARS

It's important that you do not scoff at any of your child's beliefs and that you show you take her feelings seriously. If she's worried that there's a ghost in her bedroom then look for it with her to reassure her that it's not there – while being careful not to show that you believe the room might be haunted, with a gentle 'There aren't any ghosts.' What you must encourage is that she ask you or tell you about what is frightening her or worrying her or if she isn't sure about something.

One little boy, Daniel, spent a week at school having accidents, hurting himself and even hurting other children, which was quite out of character. His mum knew something was wrong and asked him what it was. Because Daniel trusted his mum's reactions he could tell her, 'I don't think you love me any more.' His fear resulted from the fact that it was his new baby sister's christening that week and his mum had spent all her time making arrangements and trying to get through all her usual tasks. She hadn't been able to pay the usual amount of attention to her son. But because he felt able to confide in her, he told her what was wrong and she was able to reassure him. The accidents and the bullying stopped immediately.

LOOK FOR THE HIDDEN MESSAGE

So children may not always tell you something by speaking. They may feel they can communicate something in another way – maybe their vocabulary won't allow them to spell it out, maybe they haven't worked it out in their minds in a clear enough way to tell you or maybe they're worried about what your reaction might be.

One 2-year-old boy whose mother was expecting another baby was given a doll's 'family' to play with which included a mummy, a daddy, a child and a baby. The toddler carefully picked the baby out of the set and placed it under the sofa. Then he started playing with the dolls which were left. He was telling his parents how he felt about the newcomer about to enter his world. He wasn't wrong to feel that way, he wasn't right to feel that way – that's not the point. The toys had allowed him to express his negative feelings and had allowed his parents to understand how he felt. Rather than just trying to buy him off with toys and added attention and compelling him to like the situation he was about to find himself in, his parents could now put themselves in their son's position. Just as play therapy is used for children who've been through huge traumas to allow them to act out what's happened to them (which is very therapeutic as it helps them release their emotional tension) so using toys, drawing, or acting out scenarios helps other children faced with big changes in their little worlds to cope with them better.

LET'S TALK

It's important that you don't discourage your child from expressing her worries, thinking that if you both ignore them they'll go away. Those fears will just be repressed. In any case, you want to get your child into the habit of discussing her concerns with you.

This will help her tell you about the things which are most difficult to talk to you about, maybe because she doesn't understand what they are herself and doesn't know how to express them to you.

TALKING ABOUT SEX

Answer all early questions you're asked by children about their bodies and about sex. As child psychologist Dr Richard Woolfson points out in his articles on the subject, if you don't you will be communicating to children the message that it is a subject that is taboo and secret. You want your children to be open with you and confide in you if they need to. They won't tell you that someone is interfering with them if they think they'll be talking about something that you disapprove of and you will think they're dirty for discussing it. The answers to their questions can be very simple. In answer to 'Where do I come from?', for very young children a perfectly adequate answer is 'Mummy's tummy'. An adequate answer is not, 'We'll talk about this when you're older', followed by an embarrassed silence.

The answers we give them now, the way we treat them now and the way we look after them now, will all be so important in the years ahead. Use terms you feel happy with and not embarrassed with. Talk it over with your partner first if need be. If your child is grown up enough to ask any question she is grown up enough to receive an answer. It's up to you to work out how much to tell her and how much she'll understand. If you won't discuss it when she's young and wants you to tell her, it will be very difficult to talk about it and to get her to communicate with you about it when she's older.

SEXUAL ABUSE

It can seem hard to a loving parent to believe that anyone could even think of abusing a child so young, but it does happen. Even babies have been known to be abused so it's never too early to be vigilant. We've already outlined some of the signs to watch for but it's also important for parents of children who haven't been abused to teach them about their bodies and about not keeping bad secrets and not always doing what adults tell them to do if it's something they don't understand and which makes them feel uncomfortable.

Sexual abuse is one of the areas in which the 'true communication' we referred to in our first chapter is so very relevant. If your child is indicating either by saying it outright or with her body language that she does not want to be with a certain person, you must ask her why and not just decide she's 'playing up'. Of course, she may be, but there may just be something more sinister behind her behaviour. The true communication is of course additional to noticing the obvious physical signs that there has been abuse.

If your child says she doesn't want a particular babysitter or shrinks from him or her, try to find out why. There may be an innocent explanation. There may not. If your child is shrinking away from a man in a swimming pool, the same is true again.

GIVING THE WRONG MESSAGES

It's also worth asking yourself whether you should be forcing young children to 'Give Uncle John a kiss' when they don't want to. We may inadvertently be telling them that kissing isn't something we want to do, an expression of love, it can be something we don't like which we're instructed to do. Perhaps this is something we should allow children to negotiate. Give them a choice. There's nothing wrong with the message that sometimes people want to kiss us and we don't want to kiss them so we shouldn't have to. It may come in useful as they grow older, too.

Telling children to beware of strangers is one thing; telling them to beware of all the grown-ups they know – and most child abusers are known to their victims – is quite another. We do not want to destroy all the confidence and security they have. Instead, experts recommend you teach children about their rights as individuals and when they can say 'No' to grown-ups.

Kidscape, the child safety organisation mentioned earlier, recommends a Good Sense Defence charter of information for you to teach your child, and as soon as you feel she is old enough to understand, you should communicate these points to her. It's called the Kidscape Code for parents.

KIDSCAPE CODE FOR PARENTS

Children need to know how....

To be safe
Teach children that everyone has rights, such as the right to breathe, which should not be taken away. Tell children that no one should take away their right to be safe.

To protect their own bodies
Children need to know that their body belongs to them, particularly the private parts covered by their swim suits.

To say no
Tell children it's all right to say no to anyone if that person tries to harm them. Most children are taught to listen to and obey adults and older people without question.

To get help against bullies
Bullies usually pick on younger children. Tell children to enlist the help of friends or say no without fighting – and to tell an adult. Bullies are cowards and a firm, loud NO from a group of children with the threat of adult intervention often puts them off.
In cases of real physical danger, children often have no choice but to surrender to the bully's demand. Sometimes children will fight and get hurt to protect a possession because of the fear of what will happen when they arrive home without it. 'My mum will kill me for letting the bullies take my bike. It cost a lot of money.' Tell children that keeping themselves safe is the

most important consideration.

To tell

Assure your children that no matter what happens you will not be angry with them and that you want them to tell you of any incident. Children can also be very protective of parents and might not tell about a frightening occurrence because they are worried about your feelings.

To be believed

When children are told to go to an adult for help, they need to know they will be believed and supported. Although sometimes an immediate reaction is to say 'I told you so', this will not help the child to resolve the problem. It could also prevent the child from seeking help another time.

This is especially true in the case of sexual assault, as children very rarely lie about it. If the child is not believed when he or she tells, the abuse may continue for years and result in suffering and guilt for the child.

Not to keep secrets

Teach children that some secrets should NEVER be kept, no matter if they promised not to tell. Child molesters known to the child often say that a kiss or touch is 'our secret'. This confuses the child who has been taught always to keep secrets.

To refuse touches

Explain to children that they can say yes or no to touches or kisses from anyone, but that no one should ask them to keep touching a secret. Children sometimes do not want to be hugged or kissed, but that should be a matter of choice not fear. They should not be forced to hug or kiss anyone.

Not to talk to strangers

It is NEVER a good idea to talk to a stranger. Since most well meaning adults or teenagers do not approach children who are by themselves (unless the child is obviously lost or in distress), teach children to ignore any such approach. Children do not have to be rude, they can pretend not to hear and quickly walk or run away. Tell children you will never be angry with them for refusing to talk to strangers and that you want to know if a stranger ever talks to them.

To break rules

Tell your children that they have your permission to break all rules to protect themselves and tell them you will always support them if they must break a rule to stay safe. For example, it is alright to run away, to yell and create a fuss, even to lie or kick to get away from danger.

Don't deliver such a harsh message that your child will lose all trust in everyone. She may need to turn to a stranger for help one day and she shouldn't be terrified when she does that — she should just know her rights as outlined above. Do teach her, though, to go to a woman or someone in uniform if she needs to talk to a grown up. Unless she's really under threat, there's no need to teach her to be aggressive or to get into shouting matches – she only needs to be firm. This is something you can practise in little charades at home. It will give your child practice and confidence in saying, 'No, I don't want to do that', 'My mother won't let me', 'I'm going home now', 'My father's just round the corner'.

IGNORANCE IS *NOT* BLISS

You may feel that you really don't want your child to think about such horrible things as 'stranger danger' and sexual abuse. And right enough, most children will not be abused or kidnapped. But in this as in every other area of safety, forewarned is definitely forearmed. If you keep your child in ignorance of the bad things in life it will make her all the more vulnerable to them if they threaten her safety.

You may feel that your child cannot be harmed in this way: she is always with you or someone you trust. But there will sometimes be occasions when you will not be with her, there may sometimes be occasions when the trust you placed in someone will have been misplaced. Your child must be taught to say 'No'. Said with feeling, with confidence, with complete control, it's a powerful weapon.

The key to this confidence, the key to your child believing what you say and confiding her fears in you, is that she has complete trust in you. Through the way you communicate with her she will be able to sense that you really love her and that you will whatever she does or says, and the security that gives her will enable her, more than anything else, to help herself keep safe – to accept what you say is right or wrong and to start to take responsibility for her own safety.

Remember, children are eager to find out about the world around them. But they need to know about the nasty things which can hurt them as well as about the nice things which won't and which are such an important part of having a happy, fun-filled childhood. Children want to learn. While they're so young it's up to you to make sure they learn the right things.

Chapter Six
DANGERS FACED BY THE 5-10 YEAR OLD

WIDENING HORIZONS

This is the time of big, big changes for your child – and for you too. Your child will be starting school. And if you either don't work or work part-time you'll have to get used to not having her about so much. If you work full-time there are going to be different problems, such as how to get her to and from the place that's going to be the second centre of her miniature world.

For the 5 to 10-year-old, home and home life will still be very important. She'll still depend very heavily on the comforts of being with you and of being in the environment she's grown in and knows so well. We're not trying to say that everyone's home life is as idyllic as that shown in commercials – in reality no one's is – but children will still be seeing their homes as the focal point of their lives, and those inside will be the people they feel closest to and from whom they will still seek attention and affection.

But this is also the age when your child will want to start to become that bit more independent. It's inevitable that with starting school and experiencing new people and new situations, your child will get more and more curious about the wider world around her and will want to explore it more for herself.

This is a gradual process for children. Of course it won't all happen on her 5th birthday. Most of the change won't happen until much later when she feels happy about and comfortable with her new status as schoolgirl and so is ready to explore further.

TAKING STOCK

But talking about birthdays, it's worth using them as a time to take a fresh look at your home through your child's eyes. Every year you could go round the house and check that mirrors don't need raising, and whether shelves are convenient for your child to reach – or not to reach, depending on what's on top of them. Now your child is getting more independent, it's a pity if she always has to ask you to pass her her toothpaste when she's capable of brushing her own teeth. Why not keep the toothpaste on a lower level so she can carry out the whole operation by herself? Your child could join you on the tour and give her opinion of it all. Birthdays are days she'll feel big and grown up so it's a good time for this to take place.

BIG CHANGES

This is a very big age group to cover and ways of keeping children safe will change from one end of it to the other. At the 5-year-old end you'll be wanting to keep kettles well out of the way. At the 10-year-old end you'll be wanting them to be in easy reach of an eager youngster wanting to make you a nice cup of tea.

Children will be wanting more and more independence but of course there is however a complicating factor. Life isn't that straightforward. We all know of the dangers which mean that we cannot give our children a free rein to come and go as they please and do anything that comes naturally to them or that they want to do. Whether it's the threat from the ever-increasing traffic on our roads or the ever-present threat from strangers – a tiny minority of strangers but still a minority which cannot be ignored – our children need our guidance and protection and we can allow them the independence they're beginning to want only gradually.

But we must allow them to develop in this way. It's no use keeping them shut away from the world outside – that won't help them cope with the realities of life in the years to come. What we have to do is to teach them to use their judgement, so when dangers present themselves they are able to cope by themselves. We must arm them with the information they need and the confidence they need so that they see that keeping safe is their own responsibility and they are able to do just that.

The speed with which your child will be developing new skills and interests will be quite bewildering. She'll be doing more, achieving more, wanting more out of life. You might just feel extremely proud of this and of how clever your child is, mentioning it to parents, friends and anyone else who'll listen if you get the chance. But one of our rules when it comes to child safety for children of any age is that you try not to believe your own propaganda.

KNOW HER CAPABILITIES

At 5 your child is still very young. She won't have the physical strength of an older child, nor the bravery, nor the confidence in her own reactions and intuition. In short, she won't be as streetwise. She's also likely to be clumsier with her hand movements which is also very relevant to many safety areas. So make sure you're really certain she can do something before allowing her to do it. Make sure she knows what your rules are. You could, for example, say that she can come and help you in the kitchen if you or your partner are there with her but she mustn't go and start pottering about by herself. When you see that she can handle the plate she's drying or the teapot she's pouring in a confident manner, you can think again and relax the rules gradually as she gets older and more competent.

This is also the age that children really start to get the bug for doing anything and everything that their school pals do. They might want to go round to their friends' to play video games or football. They might want to join the Brownies or the Cubs, they might want to do this sport or that sport, play a musical instrument, or go to ballet classes. There sometimes seems to be no limit to the amount of activities they can discover. But remember, children can get very tired just as we can – school by itself can be quite exhausting. And in the same way that we tend to have more accidents when we're tired and stressed, children are liable to be more clumsy and their attention can wander at vital moments, too. It's important to gauge your child's moods and energy levels where possible. In other words, don't take her to the playground if she's already tired herself out at the swimming pool – it's asking for trouble. In this way we can try to avoid tiredness-related accidents.

You, too, may feel more stressed. You might be coping with going out to work for the first time in five years, you might be coping with your usual day-to-day chores with the added stresses of fitting into them your child's new routine and the worry about how they'll get on in their school life. This stress will leave you more vulnerable to lapses in concentration, to making mistakes and to general clumsiness.

When they start to get that first slice of independence it might be seen as an easy time to relax your safety rules. Many mothers of children this age have the false notion, 'Oh, they're old enough to look after themselves', and many have seen their children suffer as a consequence. Your child attending school will give you more freedom to do what you want or need to do and more time apart from your child. But that doesn't mean she is already equipped to survive in the world of grown ups. She'll still need your guidance and, very often, your protection too.

IN THE HOME

Even when your children are at this stage of their development, safety in the home cannot be forgotten. They will be aware of danger and they will have a good idea about what will hurt them and what won't but it is still not a good idea to take their safety in the home for granted.

DANGER: POISON!

Take poisoning as one example. In recent years there have been cases of 5 and 6-year-olds having taken many toxic substances including bleach, medicines, pills, cement and mortar mix, glue, and poisonous berries. Among substances taken by 7 and 8-year-olds are bleach, white spirit, medicine, and pills. You may think your children are very sensible, you may think they are brilliant readers and so will know what not to sample. But a bottle or a packet can have more labels than Alan Whicker's suitcase and the spirit of inquisitiveness or mischievousness in some children will still lead them to go ahead and try the forbidden substance. Children, like adults, often want what they can't have and the mere fact that you're forbidding them to try something may make it seem all the more attractive. That's why it's so important to spell out clearly *why* they mustn't do something, not just to tell them they mustn't and give them no good reason. It is still not advisable to take medicines and pills in front of children in the younger bandings of this age group.

DANGERS OLD AND NEW

Because your child is bigger and taller, some of the safety rules we've already outlined become even more relevant. If you have a mirror over a fireplace that a child can just see into on her tiptoes, it's a serious hazard. She'll be less steady than an adult who doesn't have to strain to see. Don't leave ladders leaning against walls. She may think she is capable of climbing them – after all, dad makes it look so easy – but there could be a very bad accident if she suddenly slips, falls or loses her nerve.

IN THE KITCHEN

Whatever their age children must be taught not to play in the kitchen and not to touch anything in there without your say so. Children may be inclined to try to help by copying some of the tasks they see you doing – moving a saucepan from the heat, for example. They must know that you'd rather something boiled over than that they risked burning themselves. Make sure you tell them everything that definitely isn't for playing with. Children have died after climbing into spin driers before now in accidents when fun and games have gone tragically wrong. They have discovered fireworks in drawers and seen them as playthings. Together with a pal's box of matches we are talking about pretty lethal toys.

You will have to decide when your child is ready to make her first cup of tea, carry her first cup of tea, or wash her first glass. There are no set rules – all children are different. But you should watch carefully to see how capable she is, how good with her hands, and whether she *wants* to do whatever it is that you're thinking about. Start off by supervising her and she will naturally graduate to doing it by herself. Don't push her to do something she's not sure of. Accidents happen when a child is unsure of herself or scared about something. You should be just as proud of her knowing that she's not yet capable of carrying out a household task – as she's showing you she knows herself and what she can and can't achieve, and she's being honest about it – as you are when she first achieves the task, such as clearing the table by herself. As in the rest of the book, we've used the female pronoun, but the same goes for boys clearing the table too, of course!

THROUGH THE EYES OF A CHILD

Some home dangers aren't always obvious and easily recognised.

> Just recently a 5-year-old suffocated when his nose and mouth were blocked by fast-setting 'super glue' which he'd laid his hands on.

It's so important that you're still putting yourself in your child's position, thinking about the substances you have in your home and the tools and appliances you're using and the harmful effects they could have if they were misused. Children at this age can start to appear very grown up and very sensible but they are still children. It's far better not to put temptation in their way.

Check, too, that your bunk beds, banisters, gates and balconies are secure. Your child will be stronger and heavier and it will take less pressure from her if there is a weak point to crash or fall through.

SPARE TIME – DANGER TIME?

Especially with older children, it's wrong to think of accidents happening with the same regularity all year round. There are peak times. Watch out for the school holidays when children may well feel at a loose end after having such a structured routine during term times, and watch out for weekends as well. A recent survey has shown that 15% of 5 to 8-year-olds never read for pleasure at home and although girls are greater readers than boys, book popularity generally declines as children get older. Yes, there is television to entertain them. So when thinking about the possibility of accidents, take into account the times when your children are least likely to be watching television. The peak viewing time is the period from when they first arrive home from school until early evening. They tend to watch the least amount of television in August and the most in February and it often doesn't get really 'addictive' until the ages of 8 to 11.

So don't assume your child will be entertained if you just dump her in front of the telly. This is especially true if there's a whole day stretching in front of her with nothing planned and no one to tell her what to do – unlike school which has teacher to discipline her and keep her on the right, safe path. It's far more likely that there'll be a mishap in such a situation. If, however, you structure the day for her in some form and arrange things to do, outings in the park or the swimming pool or an event to attend, there's less likely to be boredom and less time for her to get into possibly dangerous mischief.

KEEPING A WATCHFUL EYE

If she's got friends round and you don't want to intrude all the time it's important to keep an eye on them even if it's by saying, 'Anyone want a drink of squash?' – a question which will give you the chance to see what they're up to without barging in. But it's possible that in this age group children will want you to be involved and interested in what they are doing and may enjoy being supervised.

Children learn so much from other children. That's why if your child is shy and very solitary the onus is even more on you to teach her safety lessons, as you will be her main source of knowledge. But what they learn from other children is not necessarily all good. We've already mentioned how quieter children tend to get much more noisy and outgoing in the company of others their own age. It's quite a responsibility in any case to have someone else's child or children in your care under your roof. So it will keep your mind at rest and their play safe and happy if you supervise to a reasonable extent. You don't need to interrogate them by asking 'What are you getting up to?', with the assumption that it's definitely something bad. A quick 'How are you getting on?' is all you need.

SELF-SUFFICIENCY...

It's also a good idea at this stage to teach and encourage your child to make her own entertainment. If you're continually ferrying her from the Brownies to her dancing lesson and then on to swimming classes, she may well not learn how to make her own fun, and that's a bad habit to get into. It could lead to long periods of boredom when she's got a break from her numerous activities. It could also lead to longer periods of boredom when she's older and no longer interested in the Brownies: she may be vulnerable to suggestions from other children to try exciting new adventures or substances which might relieve the boredom but which could do other damage. Boredom and accidents are often interlinked – your child may not be concentrating or interested enough to take care of herself. You could think you are giving your child all the privileges money can buy but she may actually be disadvantaged by all her activities in the long run – and your other children, too, might find themselves without their fair share of your attention.

... AND TOGETHERNESS

If your child's interests tend to be quite solitary ones – swimming very seriously, or learning a musical instrument, for example, and if these take up a great deal of her time, this can have a bad effect on the amount of contact she has with other youngsters. All children should be able to communicate easily with others their age. They can learn from them, may need help from them, and can find out more about life from them. They should in any case feel confident about being around people. It isn't good for them to be too isolated.

However, if your child is very keen on a particular hobby, if she's not doing very well at school but is excelling at gymnastics, or if he's doing badly at school but has the makings of a great footballer, it is very good for their self esteem and self-confidence that they can excel at something in their spare time.

For the most part mothers we've spoken to have said how relieved they feel when the car's broken down or the buses are on strike. The family has to be dependent on itself to create its own entertainment – and both children and parents can have some of their most enjoyable times in that situation.

IN THE ROAD

YOUR CHILD AS PEDESTRIAN

We must make one thing absolutely clear: we believe no child should be intentionally allowed out by herself at the younger end of this age group. Even if there isn't a road to cross on the way to the corner shop, or school, or letter box, it simply isn't safe. Experts believe children are not completely reliable in traffic – in other words, they are not as good as an adult at judging speeds and confidently and safely crossing a road – until they reach the age of 12. It is a very common mistake for adults to assume that children have more road sense and more of an ability to cross roads and negotiate traffic than they really have.

It is thought that when drivers are pedestrians, they are better than non-drivers at judging the speed of traffic and predicting what might happen. Just think how far away children are from learning to drive a car.

A very common worry for parents is working out exactly when their child should be allowed to do all or any of these things by herself. We would suggest there are various factors to be taken into account – such as whether your child really *wants* to go by herself, what the distance is, what obvious hazards there are on the way. The same dilemma exists when your child wants to go to the park or playground with her friends for the first time, to the shops with her friend for the first time, or round to her friend's by herself for the first time. Again, there isn't a strict timetable for any of this but we outline in the next chapter how best to work this out for your child and how best to protect her while you're not there.

Crossing roads by itself is a major hazard for children in this age group. Researchers at the Universities of Edinburgh and Strathclyde have said that not only can children not judge distances and speeds in the way that adults can, they also cannot judge where the real danger spots are – such as the brow of a hill or near a corner or junction – and the added risks of crossing at the wrong place. They say this second danger is not adequately spelt out in the Green Cross Code. This code is based around six points:

- First find a safe place to cross, then stop;

- Stand on the pavement near the kerb;

- Look all round for traffic, and listen;

- If traffic is coming, let it pass, look all round again;

- When there is no traffic near, walk straight across the road:

- Keep looking and listening for traffic while you cross.

This may be sufficient for young children on very quiet roads, but its usefulness by itself is limited. As one academic wisely pointed out, we don't allow anyone to drive without training and instruction, yet we tend to allow young children to cross roads without training in the judgements they must make if they're going to keep themselves safe.

The Scottish team found that children aged between 5 and 7 decide that somewhere is safe to cross if they cannot see any cars from where they are standing. The children they tested decided it was safe to cross on a hill, and near a complicated junction, because no cars were in sight. They made their judgement on how direct and short the route was, believing that if it took you less time to cross the road it would be safer for you. Even at the age of 9, children were remarkably unaware of dangerous factors and only by the age of 11 were they beginning to show a good understanding of road hazards.

The academics also point out that children are taught to wait until there are no cars in sight before they cross – but on many roads that would leave them waiting around all day. The whole business of crossing roads is much more complicated than that.

In addition, the researchers are critical of the way road safety is sometimes taught. Children are left sitting watching a video, listening to a talk, or reading a book on the subject. It's been pointed out that no one ever learned to drive a car by sitting at a desk. However good the driver's manual is, driving ability can't be truly developed until the learner driver is behind the wheel of a car. Crossing roads, too, is a practical skill. So the passive methods in which the children are not actively involved are not good enough. In many cases children may have gained plenty of knowledge in the classroom about road safety and they may be able to answer any question you can throw at them, but they don't put it into practice on the streets and their road safety skills remain at the level they were at before the lessons began.

So don't leave it to the Green Cross Code – and don't assume they're taught everything they need to know in school by the visiting community policeman. Get active! Play a positive role yourself. And tell them about subways, footbridges, zebra and pelican crossings, traffic lights, and even traffic wardens, as you see them. Tell them about safe places to cross. All of this could be of help in ensuring their journey is safe. Walk the route to school with them and explain it. If there's a lollipop lady or man on their route to school, introduce your child by name so she feels comfortable with him or her when she's making her own way to school for the first time. It will be good to know there'll be a familiar, friendly face to greet her on her way.

WHEELS!

Children won't always be on their feet, of course. Many of the fads and hobbies yours may develop have implications for home safety, including skateboards – which revived in popularity after the film *Back To The Future* – roller skates, scooters, bicycles including BMX bikes, and tricycles.

> According to a recent survey, 73% of 6 to 15-year-olds in England own bicycles. In Scotland the figure is 84%. That's a lot of bikes - and a lot of potential danger.

Way back towards the beginning of this book we wrote about the dangers of babywalkers. Part of this danger is that they enable your baby to move at the speed of a toddler which makes it far more difficult for you to keep up with her, keep an eye on where she's going, and generally keep her under control. In the same way anything with wheels on the bottom of it is bound to speed up the older child. The implications of this are fairly obvious. If she falls, the injury is likely to be more serious, and even if she becomes expert in her chosen means of transport, she is bound to be less in control than if she were walking or running along. Attention can and will wander. Unxpected obstacles can get in the way. You must take care to stress these dangers to your children if they take up any of these activities. Accidents can happen when they're still wobbly and unsure of themselves or if they become brash and over-confident and start showing off or not taking enough care.

Of course, children should not be allowed on roads on their skateboards or roller skates and you must be very strict when it comes to bicycles. There's probably hardly a child in Britain who hasn't cycled further than her mother or father will allow her, which is even more reason to push this message very hard. If you think of the dangers that adult cyclists face, think how much worse they must be for children who are smaller and therefore harder for the motorist to see. Children are also less likely to be sufficiently competent as cyclists to carry out all the necessary hand signals and obey all the road signs (and that's if they're aware of the correct procedures) and their small bicycles are less likely to have the lamps needed by law and for their own safety if their disobedient journeys are at night.

Other important instructions include not allowing your child to ride with her hands off the handlebars as a means of showing off. Tell her it's not clever, it's quite the opposite. Make sure your child has the right size bike and the seat and handlebars adjusted to the right height so that she can comfortably touch the ground with her feet when she's sitting on the saddle and she can comfortably reach the brake levers. Choose a sensible bike and ignore pleas for gimmicky designs. Although cycling on the pavement is illegal, most people accept that for small children it's safer than using the road. Make sure they are careful of pedestrians and that they don't ride off the pavement into the road without looking. Anyone, adult or child, cycling on the road needs a cycle helmet meeting the British Standard BS 6863 or another national standard like the American or Australian one.

No children should be allowed to cycle on a road before they are able to turn and look behind them and do hand signals without wobbling and before they are able to cope with traffic and the rules of the road. They should certainly not be allowed on to the roads alone before the age of 9. Even after then it's unlikely they will be as protected against danger as they should be unless they have taken and passed their cycling proficiency tests. The minimum age for this in your area could be 9 or 10. Courses are usually run in schools, often in schooltime, and sometimes after school or during holidays. They usually last a week. Even if your child passes, the organisers stress it is still the parents' responsibility to make sure their child is safe on the road – the test only means children are competent to ride on quiet roads, it doesn't mean they can charge about everywhere.

Your child may argue that she doesn't need all of this instruction - she's already a brilliant cyclist – but it is very important that she attends. You could argue it will be a chance for her to show how good she is.

It's unfortunate that there aren't really places for children who are not yet ready to cycle on the roads but too big to cycle on the pavement. That in-between age group could do with cycle tracks or special playgrounds for young cyclists. The problem is that children own bikes long before they develop their road sense and yet there's hardly anywhere for them to cycle apart from the roads. That's why parents must pay attention to this particular hobby and the hazards it may hold.

BACK IN THE CAR AGAIN

When it comes to cars, it's still very important that you strap your child in firmly. For children up to around the age of 9, an adult seat belt coupled with a booster cushion is the best idea; from around 10 years old, if you child is too tall to sit comfortably on a booster cushion, use an adult seat belt which is adjustable to allow for her smaller body. Some adjustable seat belts fit everyone from children aged $4^1/2$ or so to adult, so it's worth looking at them. Children should preferably be sitting in the back. If you will be carrying three in the back, fit a lap seat belt in the middle. Remember the lap part of the belt can injure a child if she's not on a booster cushion. An ordinary cushion may slide away and is of no use. And don't think, even at this age, that it's perfectly fine to carry your child unrestrained in the back.

> 91% of all children killed in car accidents were in the back of the car at the time of the accident. 65% of those children injured in car accidents while in the back of the car were aged between 5 and 13.

Don't risk buying second-hand child seats unless you're absolutely sure they haven't been in an accident or been damaged in some other way, and that they're right for your make of car. You may be worried about the cost of all these belts and seats. But it's better to pay less on your car and have enough cash left to spend on its safety than the other way round.

> **Did you know?**
>
> 21% of car accidents happen in school run times.

If your child and you are part of a school run with other children and parents it's worth thinking carefully about what your attitude should be if the other parents' cars do not have what you consider to be sufficient safety devices. Some of the figures in this chapter should start to convince them to invest in more.

In one recent year, the number of children killed in road accidents between the ages of 0 and 4 was around 100. The number killed between the ages of 5 and 9 was more than 130. That's not to say the risk is always more at one age than it is at another – the figures should simply remind you that cars are dangerous things. There is always a risk. We must do all we can to remove as much of this as possible.

THE REST OF THE OUTSIDE WORLD

So far so good. But there are some children who will be more inclined than others to disobey your instructions. They'll be more likely to wander off with a group of pals and explore whatever they happen to pass which looks interesting than to visit the park or pool in a well-behaved bunch.

If you think there's a likelihood of your child getting involved, it's as well to warn her of the dangers she may face. The key is to present her with a powerful message about the risks without making the activity you're describing sound exciting and 'worth a go'.

TRESPASSING

ON THE RAILWAYS

Trespassing on railway property is one such 'game' which appears to some youngsters to be more fun than strictly legal pursuits. But this can be a dangerous business as well as a law-breaking one. Recent figures show that 15 children were killed and 15 seriously injured in one year while trespassing in this way. Six of the deaths were caused by electrocution. Many of the children involved in this form of entertainment were 10 years old and under. One youngster's story is particularly horrific. A 6-year-old, together with two 4-year-olds, managed to get on to the tracks by climbing through a section of fencing which had been vandalised. The older boy was electrocuted by the conductor rail just as a train was nearing the scene. The driver had no chance of stopping and the train struck the body at high speed. There is no good reason for children of this age being unsupervised and alone and able to get up to these sorts of dangerous misdemeanours.

BUILDING SITES

Construction sites are another danger spot. Children have been killed by falling materials and equipment, falls from scaffolding or into holes, and accidents involving vehicles and other mobile equipment on site, in roughly equal numbers. Health and safety experts have found that in many cases, there were reasonably practicable steps which could have been taken by the site managers to prevent the tragedies which have happened over the years – but this does not detract from the fact that the children should not have been playing there anyway.

ON THE FARM

Farms are also full of hazards. That combination of mechanical equipment and potentially aggressive animals, together with the sheer size of many farms which would make 100% supervision of the whole area impossible, means that children should be on their best behaviour if they're meant to be there, and be told off thoroughly if they're not.

BOYS ARE NOT YET GENTS!

Watch out, too, for times when they're with you but they're not with you, if you see what we mean. At around the age of 8 a young boy will not want to go to the ladies' loo with his mum. Assaults have taken place on young boys even in the most respectable-looking lavatories – those in restaurants, for example. So if you are a mother out with your son but without a trusted male adult and your child needs to go to the loo, warn him not to talk to anybody and to call out if anyone approaches him. You should stand close to the outside door so you will be sure to hear him.

WATER SAFETY

Canals, swimming pools, lakes, rivers and the sea can all turn from harmless, pleasurable places to danger spots. Don't let your child lark about near canals, lakes or rivers. If your children are keen fishermen or have another hobby that takes them on to or near water this will be even more important advice. The water may be very cold and move much faster than expected. Even the strongest child swimmer can get cramp and find herself struggling to reach dry land. Don't forget the warnings you were given when you were young about not playing on the ice on top of lakes which could be a very thin layer indeed, not strong enough to take the weight of one or more children.

Playing and swimming in the sea is a more complicated business than it used to be, with inflatable mattresses now seen as acceptable aids to making it all more fun, together with inflatable dinghies and beach balls. Your child may be very responsible as a rule, and a very good swimmer, but she can easily fall asleep on top of her lilo and drift out to sea or simply be too busy relaxing to notice how far away from the shore she's getting. Keep a close eye on her, preferably not letting her play with inflatable mattresses or dinghies by herself.

HOLIDAYS

These water dangers should be some of those at the forefront of your mind when you're on holiday. Holidays are, of course, times when you're trying to relax, but it's important not to let your safety standards slip. Your children will probably be very excited and this can mean their usual sense of judgement might slip and accidents might happen. So be sure to take care of them. If you were sufficiently concerned about their safety to buy this book you'll know that you can only properly relax when you're sure they're safe.

If you're going abroad, take more general advice from your family doctor and your travel representative about other safety standards and health matters – should you drink the water, what injections are needed and that sort of thing. Once you're there, give your hotel room, apartment, caravan or tent a quick check, as you would if you were leaving your children with a minder in a home that wasn't yours. You'll be able to spot the dangers and warn your children of them. It may also be possible to do something about them. If you're fairly sure the glass in a French window isn't safety glass, put chairs or another obstacle in the way. If you have a balcony and it looks very unsuitable for children it might be better to ask for another room without one or see if there are any changes the manager may be willing to carry out to make it safe. Kettles and other electrical appliances are often found in hotel rooms these days and in your possibly disorganised state on arrival some items which are dangerous to children, from razors to pills, may be left lying around in their paths. Keep a watchful eye to stop yourself tempting fate.

Of course, this is just as important for younger children.

SMOKING

Don't think they're too young to even think about it. Forty per cent of boys and 28% of girls – that's four out of every ten boys, and nearly three out of every ten girls – are thought to have had their first puff by the age of 10. And one-third of all regular adult smokers say they started smoking before the age of 9. Remember – children whose parents smoke are more likely to become smokers themselves. If parents aren't worried about their children smoking, or if they strongly disapprove without spelling out why, that is also likely to encourage the habit. The anti-smoking campaign group Action on Smoking and Health says that most young smokers are influenced by their friends' and older brothers' and sisters' smoking habits. It's likely that the amount of cigarette advertising about also has its effect. So you have a lot of outside influences to fight against.

If your children start smoking it may seem to you to be less drastic a happening than if they gash themselves on broken glass or nearly drown in the local pond. But don't forget that the earlier children become regular smokers and then carry on the habit as adults, the greater their risk of dying prematurely. They're also more likely to have coughs, phlegm, and chest complaints than those who don't smoke. If you smoke, try to set a good example by giving up.

SEXUAL ABUSE

Sadly this is still a danger you'll have to keep very much in mind. Your 5 to 10-year-old may be a child to you, the thought may still be almost unthinkable, but you've still got to convince yourself that she may be a target for sexual abuse.

> The headlines and statistics may have so far concerned other people's children but **yours** must be protected too.

It seems so unfair that the fun and innocence of childhood should be corrupted in this way, but it is. And as child psychologist Dr Richard Woolfson points out, it is ironic that this threat often comes at a time when children are feeling confident and strong enough to cope with unfamiliar adults.

Some experts believe that of all children, the 7 to 9-year-old is the most vulnerable to sexual abuse.

Children of 7-9 years old have more freedom than younger children, but might be less sure what to do in new situations than older children. They may also be starting to feel that you will not believe them if they come to you for help, or they may have a distorted idea of how strong they are and how able they may be to fight off an attacker.

OTHER FORMS OF SEXUAL ABUSE

There are other forms of sexual abuse which we haven't mentioned yet. One of these is letting your child view pornographic videos, even if it's soft porn. A child is often adept at using a video by the age of 6 or 7, so if you have any even faintly blue videos don't leave them lying around where children can be tempted by them or put them on by accident. And if your child is going to another home to watch, it's worth a tactful glance at any video collection in case they've left videos of this nature within easy reach.

Another problem is obscene phone calls. From when your child first answers the phone, make sure she's taught not to answer it with her name or her phone number, just to say, 'Hello'. You don't want someone who may have dialled by chance to take a note of the number which at least sometimes may have a vulnerable victim at the other end.

Nor do you want the caller to convince your child that he's known to her – he must be, otherwise he wouldn't know her name, would he? If she's feeling at all flustered or nervous, it will be easy for her to forget she gave it to him in the first place.

So tell your child, if anyone phones and says anything that upsets her or makes her feel uncomfortable, just to put the phone straight down.

It's better to be rude than to be abused.

A note about personalised belongings

It's important that your children don't wear caps, jumpers, or any other article of clothing, and don't carry books or files or any other piece of equipment, with their names on in bold letters for anyone who spots them to read. A molester could call out, 'Hello, Robert' or 'Debbie, your mother's asked me to come and get you,' and would sound much more convincing than if he had no idea of their names.

WHAT YOUR CHILD SHOULD KNOW BY NOW

During the latter end of this age group, you may be tempted to think of leaving your children by themselves at home, but we really can't advise it. They're still much too young to be left on their own. Certainly on no account leave them overnight or for long periods of time.

There may be occasions when a child this age or younger may need to take charge – if you fall over and knock yourself out, for example. So there are some general safety rules your child should know, although all children will not necessarily know them by the ages specified in these lists. That's not anything to worry about. As long as you encourage them gently, they'll learn at their own pace.

By the age of 5 your child should know:

- Who she is, where she lives and who she lives with.
- Where she is, who she is with and who is in charge of her.

- Some of the people whose job it is to help keep her safe and how to help them.

- Safe places to play and how to play safely.

- Dangerous places and what makes them dangerous.

- Who the safe people to go with are.

She should be learning:

- To stay close to what she knows and is happy with.

- To ask for and get help.

- To say 'No', 'Stop', and 'I'll ask'.

- To tell people what has happened, when, and where and to go on telling until someone listens.

By the age of 6 and 7 she should have added to these lists of safety rules. She should know:

- Her telephone number, and an alternative safe place as well as home.

- Where she's supposed to be as well as where she is, where she's going, and where she's been. How to get out of wherever she is safely. She should roughly know the time and how long it takes to go from here to there.

- Who can help her and what the limits of that help are.

- The day-to-day hazards of where she lives, plays, and the journey to school.

- The rules of places and how to behave when she's there.

- How to recognise people who aren't safe (i.e. by their actions and behaviour, *not by their looks*).

- What can make an accident and that her behaviour can prevent some things happening.

She should learn:

- Skills which keep her safe in traffic, in and on water, in and near home, with people and on her own.

- To tell people things, to ask for help, how to make people listen, how to describe exactly what happened.

- To keep rules set by her family and other people and places unless they make her feel unsafe.

By 8 and 9 she should know:

- Where she is and the people who know where she is.

- The way out, the way in, the way home. How to contact home and an alternative safe place; how to tell the time, use a telephone, judge time and distance.

- How to get safe help, the limits of what help is acceptable.

- Day-to-day hazards and risks especially when she's away from adult supervision or help.

- What the facts are about accidents to children, when, where, how they happen, and how to report an accident or an incident.

- That keeping safe is her job as well as other people's.

- That younger children will copy her and how she keeps safe and how she takes risks.

She should learn and practice:

- The skills which keep her safe at home, away from home, alone and in groups.

- To resist pressure from her own age group or older children who want her to take risks or experiment.

- To say 'I won't take that risk', 'I'll ask', 'I'll check that out'.

- To make people listen, to explain to them and describe what happened and how she felt.

This is a useful checklist, taken from one compiled by the researchers at the University of Southampton for their primary school health education guidelines, 'Health for Life'. You can use it to check that you are guiding your child in the right direction and are helping her learn what she needs to learn. Together with the other tips mentioned in this chapter and the preceding ones, most of which have a relevance throughout childhood and even into adulthood, these skills enable children to play their part in keeping safe. Teaching them should mean that not only are you providing your child with a safe environment, but you are also helping her to keep herself safe whether or not you are there, which is what this book is all about.

You can use this list as a guideline to help her to learn to keep safe, although this is only in addition to the other categories already mentioned. Teach her how to use a phone, and a public phone. Teach her how to dial 999: you can act this out with her, one of you being the operator at the end asking which service you require, the other being the person reporting an accident, a fire or a crime.

Although you shouldn't plan to leave her alone at home, if there's an absolute emergency make sure she knows not to open the door to anyone and not to let anyone know that she is alone. You should rehearse with her small white lies, such as, 'My daddy's asleep and I don't want to wake him,' or 'Mummy's in the bath. Come back later.' Tell her always to answer the phone. It's very scary for a young child to hear a phone ring and not answer it – it makes her feel very alone. And in any case it may be you trying to contact her. But tell her never to say she's alone in the house, only to give the answers as above. If it's important, the person will ring back. If you had taken your child with you there'd have been no one there to answer the phone in any case.

Assure your child you'll be back soon, check with her what she's going to do while you're out – you could even give her a target to finish a puzzle or a book by the time you get back. This will stop her worrying about you and where you've got to and even coming to look for you. That has to be a definite 'no- no'.

When it comes to picking her up from school or wherever else she may have gone, assure her you will send no one else to pick her up - or tell her who might be coming for her. If it's likely you may miss coming to get her and may have to send someone she doesn't know – if you think you may have to work late, for example, then organise a code word between you and your child. That can be your little secret – a good secret for keeps – and she must know only to go with someone who knows the word. If she's at all worried she must go and ask a teacher or someone else's mum.

Again, that's teaching her to trust her instinct and her judgement. She's already showing signs of growing up and of knowing that she can help to keep herself safe.

Chapter Seven
COMMUNICATING WITH YOUR 5-10 YEAR OLD

READY, STEADY, GO?

There's one big question which will be dominating your thoughts, with wide and far-reaching implications. You will want to know, 'Are they READY?'

This might mean, 'Are they ready to walk to school on their own?'. It might mean, 'Are they ready to go round to their friend's with the boy next door?'. It might mean, 'Are they ready to be left alone in the house during the day?'.

It's a question you'll have to keep asking yourself and each other. As the children seek more independence, you'll have to keep personal worries to the back of your mind as you try to weigh up how ready they are to be unleashed on the big wide world. On the other hand you may feel it would make your life an awful lot easier if your son or daughter could nip down to the shops for you or take themselves to school. But again, you should not let that colour your judgement. Your first thoughts when deciding whether your children are ready must concern them and not you.

It might help you in the immediate future if you can put your feet up for a well-deserved rest while your child goes out to buy you that pint of milk you need. But it won't be so relaxing for you if your child really wasn't ready for such a journey and gets into some sort of trouble or danger. It's hard to think of anything more terrifying for a parent than to be sitting at home worrying about – or searching the streets desperately looking for – a child who hasn't come home, who may have got lost, who may have got into mischief, or who may have been led astray.

THE RIGHT MOTIVES

Your first rule when deciding whether your child is ready to do something has to be whether she really wants to do it and whether you feel she's ready to do it. If the matter in question is that she wants to walk round the corner to post a letter by herself, she should want to do it because she feels grown-up enough to go by herself. Don't put pressure on her – we don't want to force children to do something they're scared of because they feel they would get your approval if they went through with it. They shouldn't do it because they want to get away from everyone rowing and shouting at each other at home or because it gives them a chance to go and torment the stray dog in the street outside.

SAY WHAT YOU MEAN

You must talk her through it. Do the journey with her, and on several occasions let her walk the last bit on her own while you watch. This means it won't be so unfamiliar for her. Tell her exactly what she's got to do and then tell her to come straight home. Children of this age will still be taking things you say quite literally. One mother we've spoken to gave her children instructions to come home by themselves from school because she couldn't meet them one day. She knew they were sensible enough to do this and not to talk to strangers or accept a lift or a present from anyone they didn't know. But she didn't tell them to come *straight* home, and they decided to stop off at the local playground on the way. They were immaculately behaved at the playground and honestly didn't believe they'd done anything wrong at all. Meanwhile their mother was, not surprisingly, in a terrible state, waiting at home for children who didn't arrive until an hour after they should.

The lesson here is never to presume your child understands what you haven't told her. Make your instructions absolutely precise.

GET INTO PRACTICE

Back to the question, 'Are they ready?'. Whatever it is you're thinking about and wherever she's headed, her first solo trip would obviously be one she has made with you many, many times so she would be very confident of the route she was about to take. When you do the journey with her you could ask her to decide when you should both cross the road. If necessary get her to do the journey with you walking some steps behind to keep an eye on her. And you should have given her plenty of practice to do whatever the task is at the other end – even if it's just posting a letter into a post box or buying a loaf of bread. It's important she's not worrying about anything as trivial as whether she's got enough money, or what to do if she hasn't. She must only be thinking about taking care of herself. So if you're sending her to buy several items at the shop, make sure she's got a list so she doesn't worry about forgetting one of the things you need.

Get her used to handling money. If you're on the bus together, let your child ask the driver for the tickets, hand him the cash and pick up the change. Let your child spot when your stop is approaching and either ring the bell or tell you it's time to go. Let her ask the shopkeeper for what you've agreed can be her treat in the family shopping such as her favourite packet of sweets – or allow her to find it from among the crowded supermarket shelves. In this way she'll gradually feel happier and more confident about operating on her own. You should soon know when you're no longer needed - when she's running ahead to the post box without you, for example, and stopping, looking, and waiting automatically at the smallest and quietest of side roads for you to catch her up.

BUT WHAT IF...?

It's a good idea to go through all possible eventualities, however unlikely they may seem to be. What would happen if she fell over and hurt herself very badly? What if someone stopped his car and asked her directions? What if someone she didn't know came up to her and asked her to help him find his lost dog or cat? What would she do if it suddenly started to pour with rain? What would she do if a big boy came and asked her to hand over her money?

You're not trying to frighten her or interrogate her, you're trying to keep her safe. Using the old 'What If?' game, you're educating her about possible dangers. The idea isn't to make her terrified of anything and anybody, it's to let her know the sort of things she might come across and how best she should deal with them. It's giving her the self confidence to deal with any incident in the most sensible fashion, to follow your rules but also to follow her own instincts.

> Remember, if you don't tell your children about nasty people or problems they might face it doesn't mean your children will be happier and safer. It is a lack of information which makes children vulnerable to crime.

The message you should be giving her is that she shouldn't stop and speak to anyone she doesn't know or trust. Adults rarely ask children for advice or directions; it would be far more usual for them to ask other adults if they're really lost. So it's not rude for your child to pretend she hasn't heard or to say, 'I don't know.' If an adult wants a child to do anything she must have the confidence to say, 'No', even if she's generally been taught to be respectful and polite to adults. Maybe at the age of 9 your child is old enough to give directions, but tell her to keep well away from a person or from the vehicle. She must be more than an arm's length away, yards rather than feet, just in case. And if she doesn't want to answer, she doesn't have to. The person asking isn't going to know if the child really does know the way to wherever they want to go or not.

Your child must also know that you won't be angry if a bully took her money away – you'd much rather she came back safely. But if there are other people around and she has the confidence to tell the bully to go away, she must use her own instincts on that. The most important message here is that her safety is the most important thing to you and to her.

To help your child use her own judgement and her own instinct, it's important you play the 'What If?' game properly. Don't treat her answers as 'right' or 'wrong', but examine what she's said with your next 'What If?' question so she can build up for herself a picture of what to do and what not to do.

So if the original question was, 'What if you were on the bus to school and you were day-dreaming so you didn't notice you'd missed your stop?', your child might reply, 'I'd get off at the next stop and walk back.' But then you might say, 'What if the next stop is a long way away and you don't know where you are when you get off?' Your child might eventually come round to the decision, 'I'd tell the conductor/driver what I'd done and ask him what to do.' So she can be proud of having worked out for herself a much safer conclusion to her problem. It is far better to ask a man in uniform to help her than to find herself in a strange place, probably panicking, possibly tearful, and having no one to turn to.

You could still carry on the 'What If?' game: 'What if the driver stops at the next stop and you think you know where you are, so you get off; but you don't remember his instructions for getting to school?' The answer you should encourage her to get to is that she would ask anyone she saw in uniform such as a police officer or traffic warden or lollipop man, and if she couldn't see anyone like that she should ask someone else's mum or another woman for help.

In fact the whole idea of being stranded in a strange place will probably be so worrying for your child that the thought by itself might be enough to stop her day-dreaming on her way to school.

If your child wants to go out with a group of others her age then it's still important for you to talk them through exactly what they're going to do – this will mean it won't be a totally new experience for them, they'll have done the journey in their minds before they go. If they want to go to the playground, ask where they're going to cross the road, what they would do if it suddenly started pelting down with rain, what they would do if one of them hurt herself badly. Some of the lessons you should be getting across with these questions are that they should stick together and not leave anyone by herself; they should only approach trusted people to help them; and they must remember to follow all their usual safety rules, even if it's at the expense of getting a soaking – if it's raining, they must still remember to cross the roads carefully, for example. You're not meant to be interrogating them, you should be encouraging them to think it through. Your tone should be, 'Let's think about what might happen.' This will make it easier for them to use their common sense and make decisions when and if the time comes.

UNDER PRESSURE

It can be difficult for mothers to let go at a time like this. You can feel pressured by the group of children saying, 'Our mothers have already said we can go,' so it would seem unreasonable for you to refuse her permission. With your safety checks, you shouldn't be trying to show up or embarrass your child in front of her friends. You are simply showing your concern. And if you do it in a tone and in a way that suggests they'll have much more fun and much less to worry about if they listen to you, the whole group of them might have reason to thank you.

ACHIEVING A COMPROMISE

There's another lesson to be learnt from this situation and that is that where it's reasonable you should always be prepared to negotiate. Your child might have good cause to resent you if you refuse her permission to join her friends in doing something that all other mothers have agreed on. It will make you seem unjust and unfair in her eyes. Compromise in a way that will make you feel happier about what she wants to do. You may have an uneasy and worrying couple of hours waiting for her to come back in one piece, but all parents know that worry at some point in their lives.

So if your daughter and her friend want to cycle to another friend's home, and you don't like the idea but another part of you believes they are sensible enough to do the journey, put sensible limitations on what they want to do. Tell them you'd prefer it if, once they get to the main road, they both get off and walk the rest of the way. That will show your concern and will seem to them to be reasonable and you will not be behaving in a way that's restrictive and overbearing.

You could ask them, 'What if you had a puncture?' and, 'What if it started pouring with rain?'. With the second question you'd obviously want them to know to shelter in a shop doorway rather than under a tree which could be struck by lightning.

MAKE THE PUNISHMENT FIT THE CRIME

All children do misbehave at some point and may eventually disobey you, perhaps when they get very sure of themselves or if they become heavily influenced by another child. It's important then to make the punishment fit the crime. If your child has been told not to cycle in the main road and she's spotted doing it then don't over-react by, for example, banning her from going out for a month. It would be far better to take away her bicycle and lock it up for a few days. You'll find this is easily the best punishment possible. And however much she begs and pleads and reassures you that she'll never do it again, it's vital that you stand your ground and don't give in until your deadline has been reached. There are far too many examples of parents who come down very heavily on their children for misbehaving but then don't stick to the harsh punishments they've doled out. But parents must be seen to be completely in control of safety matters. Make a ruling, stick to it, and make sure it's a ruling your partner will stick to as well. You don't want to be in the situation where one of you is being the disciplinarian and the other is giving in to a child's pleas.

No, the bike ban is a ruling which won't be open to negotiation, but you know and your child knows in her heart of hearts that it was a reasonable thing for you to have done. But, as we've said before, if your child does misbehave it's as well to try to find out why. Is she seeking attention from you that she's not getting otherwise? Is she afraid of looking stupid or cowardly in front of other children?

BE REASONABLE

It's vital that your child feels happy about saying the words, 'My mum doesn't let me do that' or 'I don't usually do that at home' without feeling threatened or silly. She might have to say that to other children, she might have to say it to other children's parents. The only way to make sure your child has enough confidence to say those words is to make sure she believes that you're reasonable and that what you say is reasonable, and that she realises your sole motive for the restrictions you place on her behaviour is that you care.

You could explain to her something you remember from your childhood. Maybe there was a child in your street who wasn't called in for tea at the same time as the other children and who wasn't called in for bed like the other children were. The others didn't want to go in because they were having a great time playing together but they had to go in because their mums and dads told them to. They were so jealous of the little boy who was allowed to do whatever he wanted and didn't have to go in. But what they didn't know was that *he* was jealous of *them*. It was fine being out when the other kids were there to play with and talk to, but once they'd been called in he'd get bored and lonely. It wasn't so much fun riding your bike or kicking your football when you were by yourself. He longed for someone to call him in and give him a hot dinner and tuck him up at nights. The other children thought he was the luckiest boy in the street but really he was the unluckiest and the unhappiest.

If your child believes that you are reasonable and that you care, it will be much easier for her to confide in you if she's worried that she's done something wrong or there's something she wants to talk to you about. If she trusts you and your reactions, for instance, she might be able to tell you that your neighbour has been touching her in a way she doesn't like, and made her promise not to tell. She might be very worried that it's wrong to break a promise to keep a secret or that you won't believe her, unless she has this trust in you. She might worry that you won't believe her motives in breaking a promise, that you might not believe them or might not understand them.

Your child might feel the same way if she is being bullied at school. Secrets are very important to a child of this age. They make her feel big and grown up. If she breaks a secret in her own mind, she has broken a code of honour, so it's important to show her you'll listen to her, and ask her what her opinions are before taking any action. If she doesn't want you to say anything to the school, you could ask if she'd mind you talking to the other parents about it.

She'll need reassurance that she's done the right thing by telling you. She'll get that if you tell her she's done the correct thing, but she'll also get it if she sees you have listened to her and if she understands why your reaction is as it is, and why you're taking the actions you are.

It's important that you show her you are able to see things from her point of view and that if she is trying to be good by doing something you will appreciate that. A good way of getting this across is to repeat a story we've heard which one Sunday School teacher tells the children in her class. In fact it is two stories about two broken tea cups.

TIME FOR TEA?

The first story is about a little girl (or boy) who wants to go out to play but her parents don't want her to. They think it's going to rain and she'll get very wet. There might be thunder and lightning and she might find that she wants to shelter under a tree, which we all know is a very dangerous thing to do. Or she might get very cold and wet and end up feeling ill and not being able to go to school or play with her friends because she'll be too poorly. But she thinks her friends are playing outside and they're having a great time; she thinks they're laughing and joking and playing with all their favourite toys and all their favourite games. She's so angry that she can't go out with them that she picks up an ordinary cup that's only worth a few pence which is used for tea and coffee every day, and smashes it against the wall and it breaks into tiny pieces.

· · · · · · ·

The second story is about another little girl who decides to make her mum a cup of tea because it's her mum's birthday. Her mum and dad are still in bed and she wants it to be a big surprise. So she goes into the kitchen and puts the kettle on, which her mum lets her do. Then she goes to the cabinet in the living room where she knows her parents keep their very best china and takes out the most beautiful cup and saucer that you've ever seen, which has the most beautiful flowers and patterns on it. She carefully makes the tea and then, with both hands, she picks up the cup and tiptoes up the stairs to her parents' bedroom. But just as she gets to the top of the stairs she trips and falls and spills the tea all over the floor and breaks the beautiful cup.

· · · · · · ·

You then ask the child – children of around 5 or 6 are the best age for this – which little girl was naughty and whose mum and dad should be angry; which of the girls should get a big telling off: should it be the girl who broke the ordinary cup or the girl who broke the beautiful, expensive china cup?

This is a test which will tell you how much your child understands about motives and it should help her learn about being good and being naughty. You could explain that the first little girl was being naughty and broke the cup on purpose, the second little girl was trying to be good and nice to her mum and she broke the cup by accident. That's why the first little girl is the one whose mum and dad will be cross with her.

If she can be taught the difference between what's really right and what's really wrong it will go a long way towards stopping her keeping things from you because she is frightened of your reactions and of being punished unfairly.

CONFLICTING MESSAGES

But if you tell these stories and explain the rights and wrongs of them, you must carry your message through to real life and not give a child a smack for being clumsy or give in to a child throwing a tantrum because you won't allow her to do everything she wants to do. That will confuse her again.

Don't confuse in other ways either. Don't tell your child how nasty a habit smoking is and then send her to the shops to buy you 20 Kingsize. Not only will you be asking her to do something illegal, you will be getting her into the habit of going and buying them and carrying packets around. Children who smoke often have parents who smoke, but don't despair of convincing your child against smoking if you smoke yourself. Even if you don't feel you can give up smoking, there are ways for you to get the 'No Smoking' message across to your child. The mere fact that mum or dad is puffing away at breakfast time might be enough to convince your youngster that smoking isn't a glamorous thing. And that message can be reinforced by you explaining to her why you're sorry you ever started and how much money you could save and how much better you'd feel if you could stop. Never be afraid to admit you've made a mistake and that you don't want her to make the same mistake.

To avoid some of the effects of passive smoking you could decide not to smoke when the whole family is around and can't avoid your fumes – breakfast time is a good example. And you could decide to have smoke-free zones in your home – in the children's playroom or bedrooms, for example.

This illustrates again the importance of spelling out exactly what you mean. If you say, 'You mustn't smoke' to a child who is watching you do exactly what you say she mustn't, she won't know what to think. She certainly isn't likely to respect what you're saying. If you take more time to explain and talk to her as if she's an intelligent person, she is far more likely to take heed of what you say.

A QUESTION NEEDS AN ANSWER

She'll also deserve answers to any questions she asks you. If she's old enough to ask, she's old enough to get answers. If she sees something sexy or violent on the television it's not good enough for you to turn over quickly and refuse to discuss it with her. Remember, she may well know more than you think she knows already – she will have other sources of information, she'll be getting all sorts of ideas from outside the home as well as from inside it. Some of that information may be correct, some of it may be all wrong. That's why it is important for you to talk with her about whatever's puzzling her.

One of the things which will still be puzzling her is where she comes from. 'Mummy's tummy' isn't an explanation which will satisfy her for very long, although it does serve a purpose for a short time. Another wording that's been suggested for children who can understand a bit more is, 'Daddy loved mummy so much he wanted them to have a baby so he put his seed into her.' Tell her just enough, but don't give her details that she won't understand. It's generally accepted these days that it's OK to let children at the younger end of this age group see their mum or dad without their clothes on, if one of you is in the bath, for example, and if you all feel comfortable about it and not embarrassed. You may even be happy about this when your child's a little bit older. But it's vital that none of you feels embarrassed or awkward about it, otherwise it's counter-productive. In either case, answer any questions she may ask you about her body and about yours, again giving just enough information.

Use words to describe parts of the body that you and your partner feel happy with. Discuss it between you beforehand. And if you are using picture books to help your child understand, check the words and pictures the book uses carefully to make sure they're the ones you feel are right for your child.

If you are embarrassed, your child will be embarrassed too and will learn to think of sex as something which isn't natural and normal. This will also mean your child is less likely to tell you if someone is abusing her in some way. She may feel it means she is dirty and she will have to use words you do not feel comfortable with and may be cross with her for using.

AVOIDING EMBARRASSMENT

As your child moves through this age group, it's likely she will become quite self-conscious about subjects such as these. But that doesn't mean the child isn't interested. Don't force children to sit and have a formal chat whenever you're discussing something that might embarrass them. You can both be busy doing something else, washing up together, or fitting a puzzle together, and discuss it without having to maintain eye contact.

But even if you are pretending the chat is a casual one and not highly structured, make sure you get across exactly what you want to say. Don't skirt around any issue so you end up not giving your child any message at all. To avoid this you can rehearse it by talking to another adult, to your partner or a friend or to yourself. If you are embarrassed and your child is embarrassed you'll both be concentrating on the embarrassment and not on what you are trying to communicate to each other.

IMPORTANT MESSAGES

One of the messages you want to get across to children of this age about any sexual touching is that it should always be part of a caring relationship between grown-ups. As adults we know that is not always the case, even when both partners are willing, but your child does not need to know this yet. She must know that if any adult tries to touch her in any way she does not like it is her right to say 'no'. She is not a grown-up and she does not care to be touched in that way.

SOME SECRETS *CAN* BE TOLD

Remember that children have often created their own code of conduct and it might be one which bodes badly as far as safety is concerned. As we said earlier, it's likely they'll think that keeping secrets is very important – and it is an important part of the playground friendship philosophy! But you must communicate to your child that she shouldn't keep bad secrets from you. Many child abusers operate successfully because they manage to persuade their victims to keep their antics as 'Our little secret'. You must give your child the knowledge and courage to be able to break that promise and to tell you about what's been said to them.

Or, as the University of Southampton researchers conclude, your children must understand that saying 'No', even if it may seem to cause problems or threats, is not rude, thoughtless or unkind if what they are saying 'No' to is frightening and upsetting. They must understand that what people tell them could be true but it could be just their opinion or it could be pretend. There are real and pretend threats and real and pretend promises. Some secrets need to be told. Telling people is not telling tales but a way of getting help.

LEARNING TO STAND UP FOR HERSELF

When it comes to resisting bullying from people her own age or from older children at school, you will still want her to confide in you. But it may be more suitable for her to take action than for you. Check that she's walking tall – bullies often go for victims who appear to be slouching and don't look as if they are confident and will stand up to them. You could practise posture with your child in front of a mirror if you think that might help. Ask your child if she can build up allies so the bully is isolated. Even if she's with her friends and there isn't a bully in sight it's important that she has the self-confidence to stand up for herself, even if what she's saying is going against the popular tide of opinion. If the others want to go trespassing, or to play dangerous games in the road, or to go with a stranger who offers them money or other presents, it would be very pleasing and relieving to know that your child is the one to say 'No'. She must have the conviction and the knowledge which will give her influence. If the others tell her she is silly and a coward for not wanting to join in, you would want her to be able to stand up for herself and tell them they are silly for wanting to go ahead.

THE VOICE OF REASON

You don't want your child to lose friends (unless they're a really bad lot), just as you don't want her to bow to pressure and fall in with a majority she knows is wrong. The only way she will have the sort of confidence to lead others away from danger is if she is repeating a lesson she's learnt from you which has all the stature and common sense that a lesson coming from a grown-up should have. And she will only be capable of doing that and feel she has the authority to do that if she believes in you and what you say. If your child thinks she'll get a smack round the ear for even mentioning she was with youngsters near a railway or building site you've told her to keep away from, she'll gradually build up a feeling of injustice and may transfer her allegiance away from you. So be reasonable. If she was somewhere you've told her is out of bounds but if she resisted temptation to do something very naughty, she does not deserve punishment. Every child's standards slip from time to time and although hers have slipped, she has also shown herself to be very sensible and trustworthy. She has shown that although she may have broken one of your rules, she has acted responsibly and taken action to keep herself safe. No one's perfect. She should be able to feel she can share what's happened with you without you over-reacting about it. She will learn from the experience she's just had without a clout from you.

REAL FEARS

The Southampton research has also shown that some children of 6 and 7, and of 8 and 9, include 'getting told off' and 'getting in trouble' in their lists of situations which they must keep safe from. Children of this age will be even more receptive to the message that being told off by mum, and keeping safe from the people they describe as 'bad men' and 'nasty misters', are two very different things. But you can only give them that message if you are still willing to listen to all your child's fears and worries. Remember to give her time every day to express herself to you. Bedtime is often a good time.

Children in these age groups are still mentioning imaginary dangers in their lists, although not as often as younger children do. Ghosts, aliens and monsters are some of the things children believe are a threat to them, though they may be less inclined to admit this as they'll worry about being laughed at. So again it is important you listen to your child's fears and do not scoff at them or tell them they are being childish. Of course they are being childish – they are children, and they have legitimate worries and they need to have their minds put at rest.

Never forget they are children. They may seem very grown up, especially if you have younger children as well as your 5 to 10-year-old. They are still learning and developing and they still need you to show them how to keep themselves safe and to help them do it.

One of the findings of the Southampton researchers is that during the middle years of this age group children tend to find out what to do about the dangers around them.

When asked what to do about dangers, very young children say, 'Don't touch it'. And that's what we want them to say – we don't want them to touch sharp knives or hot kettles. But looking more closely at their answers when they're asked what they're keeping safe from is very revealing. They say, 'Glass to cut you'. and 'Fire to burn you'. They see, for example, cars as objects which want to hurt you. (Adults can perpetuate this myth by saying, 'Naughty table' when a child hits her head). Children of this age do not have the awareness to see that it's what *they* do that causes the danger. This only tends to come by the age of 8 or 9, and so the research points to the fact that parents should encourage this awareness.

At 8 or 9 when children are asked how they would keep safe from a kettle they stop saying, 'Don't touch it', and they start saying, 'Get someone to show you how to use it'. They realise the kettle does not *intend* to hurt them.

This is another example of the way that adults tend not to realise that children's awareness of being responsible for their own safety develops very slowly.

We've already mentioned that they list adults when asked the question directly, 'Who is responsible for keeping you safe?'. At least half of the 9-year-olds surveyed did – and it had nothing to do with the intelligence of the children concerned. Very bright children had still not grasped that they were responsible for themselves.

Noreen Wetton, co-author of the report, says that after children have listed the adults they believe are responsible for keeping them safe – from mum and dad to policeman and aunties – she responds by saying, 'So if you were going on a picnic you'd take all those people? It would spoil the picnic a bit, wouldn't it?'. That starts to get the message across.

TWICE TOLD

Your children still need guidance about day-to-day activities if they are to keep themselves safe. If you are teaching your 9 or 10-year-old to strike a match, explain exactly *why* you do it the way you do – that you strike it away from you so that sparks do not fly towards you; that you hold the match and the box firmly so you don't drop either and cause an accident; that you hold the whole lot well away from you. Everything needs to be said. Often, with children, everything needs to be said twice. They may only see the surface of meaning of something on first telling. By repeating something – and then getting them to repeat it – you help them see the meaning behind the words, and it will also give you a chance to think carefully to make sure you've said what you wanted to say, in a way you're sure your child has understood.

And be sure to make yourself available to hear your child's fears. She'll have heard so many snippets from so many quarters, it's understandable if she gets confused. 'I don't want to grow up and have sex and AIDS,' one young girl revealed to Mrs Wetton. Our children may so easily find out more than we think they know – and their knowledge can so easily be distorted.

Repeat your warnings before your child does something, repeat your road safety and 'stranger danger' messages before she goes out, for example. She may think she's bored with hearing them but she'll be very grateful to you if anything does happen. She'll have your message still ringing in her ears and ready to put into action.

SOMEONE TO TURN TO

All children at some time have convinced their parents to let them do something and have later regretted it bitterly. There's the teenager who's begged to be allowed to sleep over at the party and told mum and dad not to come and collect her and show her up in front of her friends – and then found herself with an over-friendly man she doesn't like and can't get rid of. There's the 9-year-old who persuades mum to let him take his bike to the local shops, who rides it extra carefully but who falls off after riding over a hole in the road and sees his beloved bike disappear under the wheels of a car.

Even when you think she's getting independent, she does need you to look after her, to be supportive and to be proud of her achievement. Perhaps some parents of children of this age range don't realise quite how much they're still needed.

When your child comes to you for help, give her just that. She really doesn't need an 'I told you so'. After all, in both cases you were convinced, you gave your permission. And even if you hadn't given your permission, she will still have learnt from what she's done. She is simply a child growing up. Growing up is a complicated business in which children make mistakes and adults make mistakes. Only one thing about the whole process is certain – your child needs you to help her to do it safely.

Chapter Eight
DANGERS FACED BY THE 10-14 YEAR OLD

GIVING IN TO PRESSURE

Just for a moment stop thinking about your children and start thinking about you. Think about the times you've done something you really didn't want to do but have bowed to pressure – pressure which might have come from your partner, from your parents, or from your friends.

Did you stay on at a school you hated because your mum and dad thought it would be best for you to retake exams you knew you weren't going to pass anyway? Or did you leave school because your parents said they'd rather you were doing an honest day's work than wasting your time with books, even though you could have achieved a good batch of qualifications if you'd been left to work in peace?

Have you left a job you were happy in because your partner decided you could do with the extra cash another one would provide? Have you voted in an election the way your partner or your friends did – or have you abstained and not gone to the polling booth because they haven't bothered so you might as well not bother either?

Have you gone to spend Christmas with relations in the time-honoured tradition of your family when all you really wanted was to stay at home and have a quietly festive time together, just the three of you or the four of you, or however many you have in your immediate circle? Have you longed to slump in armchairs watching Christmas 'Top Of The Pops' and the only decent film on the telly all year, rather than sit to attention and make small talk with aunties you hardly know, pretending you like the gloves they've bought you – and desperately hoping the children will put on the same show?

Let's get more specific. Have you ever gone out resolving, before the front door slammed behind you, that you wouldn't be drinking anything alcoholic that evening, maybe because you were too tired – maybe because you thought you'd had enough that week already; maybe because you were driving and you'd already had a couple of drinks at lunchtime; maybe because you were on tablets which specify on the packet they shouldn't be taken with alcohol; maybe because you feel a night out without booze once in a while never does anyone any harm? – but then you've found you've weakened in response to your host's or your mates' or your partner's entreaty to, 'Go on, just have one. One won't do you any harm,' or the almost universal response to a request for a soft drink: 'Are you sure?'

All of these examples show how susceptible to pressure and influence from other people we all are. Sometimes that pressure may be positive, sometimes it may be very negative. Sometimes it will have our interests 100% in mind. More often its motives will involve at least partly the interests of others. Sometimes that pressure will be spoken, sometimes it will be understood between you without words being necessary.

Sometimes we will be in a strong position to try to resist the opinions and influence of others. At other times we will not be fighting from a position of strength. Whichever of these is true in whichever of these circumstances, when we weaken our resolve and give in to that pressure it will sometimes be for our long-term benefit and we may live to thank the person or people who directed us towards the right course. But sometimes the advice of others will have been quite wrong and could have caused a great deal of damage and harm.

The examples above may affect people aged 15 or 16 and above – they'll affect older teenagers, adults in their 20s, parents, grandparents, and great grandparents. We are all susceptible to bowing to pressure from others. But when we do that as adults, we should be in quite a good position to see the possible outcomes of doing so. We should know only too well, because of all the publicity campaigns, that if we drink one over the limit and then drive home, not only do we risk losing our driving licence and finding ourselves with a criminal record, we also risk causing damage, injury – or worse – to ourselves and to others. Our alcohol intake will mean we won't be at our sharpest and most perceptive and our driving will not be at its best. The choice is ours.

When children bow to pressure from the people they mix with, they won't have that wealth of knowledge which most of us have built up simply because we've lived longer and seen more. The choices they make in their early years could, to a far greater degree, be made from a position of ignorance. They may be thinking too much of the short-term benefit of, say, trying a drug or going somewhere you've told them is out of bounds, and not the long-term effects. They are far more vulnerable to being led astray.

It's our job as parents to arm them with the information they need. Without our help it's very likely they'll be lacking in an adult perspective and adult guidance. It's also our job to make sure we understand that while we may have brought our children up to be well behaved, they are open to influence and they can be pressurised to an even greater extent than we can, because they won't be quite so aware of the implications of whatever it is they're being pressed to do, or to try or where they're being pressed to go. So our children need to be forewarned, and we need to be open-minded.

GROWING UP FAST

However, we can only forewarn if we ourselves know the facts and the dangers that might surround our youngsters. And we can only forewarn in time if we keep an open mind as to how quickly our children are growing and how adult they are becoming.

All the evidence from all the surveys and all the figures from all the questionnaires not surprisingly point to one major factor – our children are growing up all too fast! That's not a process which can be stopped in many ways. Maybe just as sprinters are getting faster and faster, world records in all sports are broken time and time again, and maybe just as Roger Bannister's four-minute mile now seems almost to be nothing more than a light jog compared with some of today's athletic times, so this is just another sign of the world progressing. It's a different sort of race – the race to encounter new and more grown-up experiences faster and earlier than previous generations would have done. But it's a race just the same. You'd get a grim look if you tried to tell an athlete not to run too fast in her Olympic final, and similarly you're not very likely to get a warm welcome to any suggestion to your children that you want them to hold back on their development and not want to reach out for the new and exciting prospects they're seeing around them.

What you can and should suggest, however, is that some of these prospects are dangerous and are not as exciting and grown-up as they think. And it's also vital to point out that life is never as simple as it seems. Just as society's many dangers mean that, although they'd like nothing more, younger children can't ride their bikes on the road or go to the playground on their own, so they too must appreciate their freedom of movement and action must be limited.

You should be able to spot the signs that your children are maturing, and maturing fast, very easily. There'll be the obvious bodily developments, of course. But there's also likely to be a change in what interests them and how they fill their days. By the age of 11 or 12, reading and drawing tend to be out as popular pastimes, and the radio and records are in. Toys are no longer important. Your sons are likely to be discussing their favourite television programmes, soccer stars and teams; your daughters are likely to be discussing their favourite pop music and pop singers. In place of toys, personal stereos, cameras, clothes and records and tapes are the order of the day. When it comes to television, the chances are – certainly by the age of 12 – they will like programmes aimed at an adult audience as much as they like children's shows.

But don't forget there's an enormous range of speeds of development in children. Some 10 and 11-year-old girls will still be playing with dolls. Some will be very mature, others will be acting like 8 or 9-year-olds. Neither is right or wrong – and it would be wrong of you to look at it in those terms. Simply respond to your own child and her rate of development.

WIDER HORIZONS

At the beginning of the age range covered in this chapter, the home will still be where they spend most of their free time. But the security and peace of mind you get from knowing exactly where they are (and that is under your roof) will gradually wane as the amount of time they spend there wanes. By the age of 11, an average of one in five boys has a regular job, mostly delivering newspapers, and one in ten girls has a regular job; one out of every three 11-year-olds claims he or she has a regular girlfriend or boyfriend; because they'll more than likely be changing school at around this point, they're likely to have further to travel. All of these three developments have safety implications which we'll discuss later.

There's also the general trend towards finding their fun away from home. All of a sudden many children feel happier standing around street corners or window shopping with their pals than sitting comfortably in front of the telly all evening. That there's more to life than what's on offer at home and at school is their major new discovery. But with it come major, new dangers which they'll need to know about for their safety, for their peace of mind – and for yours.

It's important to remember that although your children will be heavily influenced by their friends, you will still be a very influential factor in their lives. Your children may, however, judge you more by your behaviour – whether you smoke, for example – rather than what you are saying about smoking. So if you tell your children not to stay up until all hours, and then you do exactly that watching a late-night video, they'll notice.

HOME THOUGHTS

Your concerns in this area will by now be fewer and your children won't be needing your unstinting supervision. You will be only too pleased if they offer to make a cup of tea by themselves – or if you manage to talk them into it! And as we've just said they're likely to be spending more and more of their time away from home so your worries will often be what they're getting up to outside, not what they're doing inside.

It may be, however, that they're not quite as grown-up and capable of all adults' tasks as you imagine. Yes, they look as if they're getting taller every day and yes, they can show more and more signs of developing into teenagers, but that doesn't mean they can always be left to their own devices. Your 10 to 14-year-old will not have the strength of an older person and so is unlikely to have adult control if she's handling a heavy piece of equipment or taking a heavy dish out of the oven. Don't give her too much responsibility too early: she will still be far too young to operate many electric tools or mow the lawn. You won't be wasting your breath if you carry on mentioning the dangers of fire, broken glass, matches and many kitchen appliances. Your child may be in a great hurry to get out and about and so be inclined to slip up when using a sharp knife, for example – why not remind her to take extra care and take things at a reasonable pace?

And although it's important that your child does her fair share around the home, don't overload her with chores. She will have a life of her own to lead, and if you've asked her to get a bath ready for her younger brother or sister, make the dinner, and tidy up, and if at the same time her best friend rings for a gossip, there's plenty of scope here for a nasty accident – and the fault won't all lie with the child.

ENCOURAGE INDEPENDENCE

On the other hand it's important for her later independence and the smooth running of her life when she moves away from home, not to mention the amount of respect she gives you and to your home, that you don't do everything for her. If you let her take everything for granted – from the way that an egg is ready for her every morning as if by magic and the washing up equally magically does itself too, to the way her bed is miraculously made and her shoes are always miraculously clean – not only will she, in the time-honoured favourite phrase of all parents, 'treat this place like an hotel', she will also have a huge jolt into reality when you're no longer there to indulge her every whim.

The accidents may then come later in her life when she tries to wire a plug and it's something she's never had to do before, or they may come when you're unexpectedly out and all of a sudden your child has to cope. For once she is completely on her own. That might not be a disaster if all she has to do is boil an egg. It might be if there's suddenly an electrical fire. If she isn't clued up enough to do the most simple of tasks because you've always done them for her, how will she cope in a real emergency?

We come back here to the point we've already outlined several times. Children are not your possessions to be treasured by smothering them with all your time and all your energy, they're not your pets to be stroked and spoiled. They are living, growing human beings who, if you encourage them, teach them and guide them, should safely make their way to adulthood and independence.

ON THE ROAD

Road safety, too, moves on a step. Your child will be out and about more on her own, or with others her age. You won't be there to hold her hand – in any sense. Hopefully she's picked up the lessons you've taught her about crossing roads, cycling on them and not larking about anywhere near them. But that doesn't mean there aren't other lessons to be learnt.

More children are killed on the roads in the 10 to 14 age group than in either of the younger age groups 0-4 and 5-9. In one recent year 181 older children were killed, compared with 131 5 to 9-year-olds and 104 under 5s. That's a lot of death – and a lot of reasons not to be complacent.

It's important that you don't slacken on the car seat belt front, and that you encourage your children to belt-up when you're not there to check up on them. Remember that belted-up in the front is safer than sitting loose in the back. It would be unrealistic to think that your child will never travel in a car without wearing a safety strap – she's bound to find herself in circumstances where she'll have to. But if she knows to wear a seat belt whenever she can that's pretty good going.

The ages of 11 and 12 are when you're most likely to see your boys on bikes – and girls will often be using them, too. Your child should by now know the rudiments of cycling proficiency, whether or not she's done the official test, but the reminder when she leaves the house to 'be careful' is rarely wasted. She'll be under pressure from friends to stop using cycle helmets. Encourage her to carry on.

If she's using the bus, advise her to sit or stand downstairs and near the driver or conductor, if she can. If she's worried anyone's following her when she gets to her stop, tell her to stay near other people and if no one's about and she's very worried something's not right, to go and knock on a door or alert attention in another way. With trains, too, she should be sure to get into carriages where there are other passengers or where the guard is, if she is alone or with just one other person. She shouldn't be afraid of changing carriages or compartments if all the women passengers get out at one station. Explain what the communication cord is for and tell her to pull it if anyone is attacking or intimidating her, preferably when the train has stopped in a station. So many children have seen the warnings about huge fines by the emergency notices and so have failed to call for help.

Wherever she is on her own, she must be reminded to be alert and to follow her own instincts, even if she ends up making the occasional embarrassing mistake and has only imagined that a man has been following her.

One general rule about road safety also applies to other areas – water safety, for example (a surprisingly high number of anglers, 28% of Britain's 3.5 million, are boys aged between 12 and 18). As she masters skills she can become lax about the safety rules she's been taught since she was knee-high – and over-confidence can mean disaster if she's not paying close enough attention to possible danger spots such as roads and rivers. It's important that your child realises she's still vulnerable and that it isn't adult to take risks with her own health and safety or the health and safety of those she's with.

THE BIG WIDE WORLD

Different children and teenagers will be ready to venture out on their own at different ages. There can be no hard and fast rules. And we've already discussed in a previous chapter how to decide if and when your child is confident and adult enough for whatever activity is in question. What will be true for almost all children, however, is that they are bound to be seeing more of the world and living more of their lives without you to watch over them.

Journeys to school are likely to be longer and might involve other modes of transport than your child has used before. The school itself might be a big, unfamiliar place full of bigger, more unfamiliar people than she's used to. And placing school to one side, your child will want to stay out later, and in time she'll want to go to new places such as youth clubs, discos, cafés, and the pictures with her pals. We'll talk in the next chapter about how best to work out what she should be allowed to do and how best to help her avoid possible dangers even though you won't be there. In the meantime it's vital that you know what those dangers are. Your children may be confronting them whether you like to confront that thought or not. To you it may seem almost unthinkable that an older chap at the youth club disco might try to persuade your 13-year-old daughter to go 'all the way' with him, or that your 11-year-old son might be offered glue to sniff by boys at school. But, although those thoughts aren't pleasant ones, it won't help your child to protect herself and to say 'No' if she isn't aware of the dangers in the first place – and if you delude yourself into thinking these things only affect other people's children, not your own.

She may not know whether what she's being asked to do is wrong, especially if the person trying to talk her into it is very persuasive and very clever. She's certain not to know the implications of what she's being asked to do and the extent of the harm she could do to herself as a result if you haven't helped her learn this. Here are some of the areas which should concern you as parents.

STAYING OUT LATE

This is the perennial arguing point for parents and children – What time is late? What time is fair? What time is bedtime? We think it's important that all of this is negotiated between you, but that you teach your child rules which will keep her safer when she's out at night. Tell your child:

- Tell us where you're going and who you're going with.

- All we are concerned about is your safety and if anything bad happens, even if you feel guilty or bad about it, you must still ring us or someone we both know and trust who has a phone and tell us where you are so we can come and get you.

- If there's a real need, you can get a taxi home and we will pay at the other end. And make sure you know how to make a reversed charge phone call.

- We will all agree on a time you must be home and make sure you stick to it.

- Whatever your friends say, don't do anything you don't feel comfortable with. You don't have to give reasons – it is your right to refuse to take part in whatever they're doing.

- Whatever anyone says, your body is your own and you don't have to do anything you don't want. (Daughters must know that even if they've kissed and cuddled with a boy it is their right to say that they don't want to go any further. A boy has no right to force a girl to do anything. She shouldn't believe him if he says she 'led him on').

- Stay together as a group – don't drift away from the pack.

- Use your instincts to tell you if the group is doing something you don't approve of – maybe taking a stolen car, maybe sniffing glue. If so, leave with anyone else who doesn't want to get involved.

- Keep away from unlit streets, yards, and alleyways. If anything seems at all threatening, run for help to the nearest person or the house with lights on. If anyone tries to steal anything from you, it's better to give it up if your safety is in danger.

- Don't hitchhike. And don't accept lifts from strangers.

- Keep away from places you know may mean trouble, such as amusement arcades and rowdy cafés. Don't go into pubs.

Some of these rules will apply to the younger children in this age group but most will apply to the older who will be allowed out longer. 'Street life' becomes very important to children aged 13 and over. You don't need to worry about when your child will be ready to venture out – your child will tell you that. Your job is to curb excesses which come with youthful enthusiasm, teach her to take care of herself, teach her about the dangers she may face, and have confidence in her ability to look after herself while still turning to you for help if that's what she needs.

RUNNING AWAY

This is a problem for children whose main complaint tends to be that 'no one ever listens to me'. They can be suffering in a major way, maybe from sexual abuse, physical abuse, problems at school, rows and arguments, or maybe there is drunkenness or another major problem in the home. Or they may just be bored and feel they haven't been able to communicate that to anyone at home or that no one is able to alleviate that for them where they are. Running away is a show of independence and a shot at independence at too early an age for it to be healthy and viable. And it affects some quite young children but also 13 and 14-year-olds and above.

Feeling unloved, problems with step-parents, or parents divorcing, are other reasons children give for leaving home. Of course you and your partner will have to examine your own attitudes critically and see to what degree your child's fears or criticisms are justified. If communication has broken down to this degree you'd be well advised to seek advice from outside the family, maybe from a social worker or voluntary organisation to help you try to talk together again. More immediately, here's what to do if your child has run away:

- Call the police – they have a duty to follow up every case reported to them of missing juveniles.

- Don't go and look for her yourself unless you have a pretty good idea of where she is. It's better to wait by the phone for her to contact you, which is most likely what she will do.

- Don't assume she's gone to London. Think of other friends she could be with, maybe closer to home.

- Do welcome her home and talk things through, preferably with the help of others outside the immediate circle, even a favourite teacher at school. You want someone neutral to help get matters into the open, not simmering under the surface ready for the next outburst and walk out. Tell your child her leaving has had an effect, and listen to what she has to say. You don't want her to run off again and maybe get involved in prostitution or some other unpleasant racket.

SEXUAL ABUSE

So many wide-ranging and differing lessons are being taught about this these days. But maybe at the back of all our minds we still think about the 5-year-old being offered sweeties outside the school gates when we're a few minutes late picking her up.

It's important your 10 to 14-year-old is aware that she's still at risk. Her body may be maturing into that of an adult but that doesn't mean adults have the right to treat her as an adult sexually. However confident your child is and however grown up she feels, she is unlikely to be physically strong enough to fight off unwanted attentions, so warning her about dangers should help her to keep away from risky situations.

It will also open up the subject for discussion. Children in this age group may feel too embarrassed to bring up the topic themselves if it hasn't already been raised. If your child is being continually abused and doesn't feel she can talk to you about it, it may mean she'll run away, or she could in turn start to abuse other children, even her brothers and sisters or others at school. That's why it's so important that she feels able to communicate with you and isn't scared you will moralise or blame her to make her feel dirty.

Some child abuse experts are now saying that the uproar over Cleveland and the emphasis on abuse in the home and by adults known to the children has meant that children are no longer getting the powerful messages they should be getting about keeping away from strangers. Abuse can come from people your children know and those they don't. They are not too old to be warned about both.

And don't forget to tell your child about AIDS, about other sexually transmitted disease, and about unwanted pregnancy. All of this information should both arm her if she's arguing against unwanted sexual pressure, and help her to work out a moral code for herself. You should know when your child is ready to learn about the ways of protecting herself against AIDS (by always using condoms and by having few sexual partners) and when she is ready to learn the other important facts about sex. This should mean that in the future, when the time is right, her attitude towards making love will be a more sensible one.

ALCOHOL ABUSE

This is one of the many problems which your child will face. It is not the most widespread danger affecting children in this age group, but we've already mentioned how easy it is for adults to bow to pressure and accept a drink when they've already made up their minds not to.

That pressure is also there for children curious to taste new experiences, trying to appear adult and trying to fit in with the gang.

The Medical Council on Alcoholism stresses that attitudes towards alcohol are developed very early and it believes that some form of education about alcohol should begin while children are still at primary school age. One survey has shown that half of Britain's 11-year-olds have an alcoholic drink once a week or more. It is thought that most children are drinking by the age of 14. Another study of primary children revealed that 40% of 6-year-olds and three-quarters of 10-year-olds could recognise an alcoholic drink simply by smelling it. While they were younger the children tended to disapprove of the alcohol but the older children weren't so disapproving – they were no doubt aware that members of their family, and maybe older friends, drink alcohol.

Without doubt, alcohol has become more accessible as the years have gone by. Opening hours are longer, off licence stores seem to be springing up everywhere, supermarkets have shelves crammed with wine, spirits and beer. It is inevitable that your children will know something about alcohol, they'll have seen it and watched others drinking it. So you have to decide what lessons you want your children to learn about it. It's an issue which can't be avoided.

Whatever your message is, it's bound to be a more complicated one than any message about smoking or other drugs. You're unlikely to be saying that they will never be allowed to touch a drop. A more sensible message, says the Council, is one which involves general information about alcohol and about sensible decision-making, about moderation, and about resisting pressures from their own age group and from advertisers. 'Making sure that children know the facts about alcohol seems to be a sensible minimum requirement for any education for adult life,' it says, adding that you will be helping your children make decisions about the lifestyle they wish to adopt in the future, which is a very subtle but also a very important process which starts very early.

Did you know?

Every year around 1,000 under 15s are admitted to hospital with acute alcohol intoxication.

Some of this figure will be accounted for by very young children being accidentally poisoned when drink is left somewhere they can easily reach it. But the rest will be the result of alcohol abuse by children, who can be taught that sensible use of alcohol is alright, but abuse of the stuff is all wrong.

Don't forget to look to your own drinking and the amount your partner drinks. If either of you drinks excessively the welfare of your children is just one of many good reasons to seek help. The children of problem drinkers and alcoholics suffer a great deal. As well as being at risk of being abused and neglected and of being given too much responsibility in the home at too young an age, they are more likely to drink excessively as they grow older. Sons of alcoholics are four times more likely to develop alcohol problems than other men. Children of parents who are very anti-alcohol and have an unswerving, unbending attitude, are also more likely to drink heavily than others as they grow up – whether or not their parents realise this at first.

Chronic alcoholism can cause brain damage even in quite young people. It can also damage unborn children, reduce fertility, cause impotence and lead to other sexual problems, although this should be relevant only to age groups outside the ones covered by this book.

It's true that nobody is too young to have a drinking problem of some sort. As Alcoholics Anonymous says, it's not how long you've been drinking or what you've been drinking but what drinking does to you that counts. So if a youngster is drinking alcohol to help her cope with stress, if she suffers from loss of memory because of drink, if she is getting into trouble because of alcohol, if she's drinking alone or in the mornings and if she's lying about it or proud of it, she and you should seek help.

But what is probably more relevant to this book and what should be a more widespread concern, is the side of drinking which your children probably think is less serious and not worth worrying about – but which could lead to untold harm.

Alcoholism as such – addiction to alcohol – is much less common among young people aged between 15 and 24 than it is among the rest of the population. In any case most of the young people who drink excessively below the age of 25 will be drinking less and will have learned how to drink responsibly by the age of 40. One American study revealed that young adolescents with alcohol problems do not as a rule become alcoholic adults (although there is a slightly greater risk of this happening to them than to other adolescents). It's well known that the young drink more than older people and their drinking patterns calm down as the years go by.

So what's more important for you to understand and to communicate to your children are the other dangers – the more immediate ones, the ones that result from over-drinking carried out as a form of showing off or bravado, or the misguided belief that it is something clever and grown-up, or something that's worth indulging in just to silence everyone who's been urging them to try it.

These are, to adults, the more obvious, immediate effects of drinking too much. They include the way alcohol will cloud judgement and make accidents and injury more likely, the way it causes arguments, fights, illness, debts, and poor work performance. Remember, we could be talking about your child here. How much better it is for parents to encourage a sensible attitude towards alcohol in the first place.

In one magazine survey only 12% of 15 and 16-year-olds – that's just one in eight – thought that alcohol could be harmful. This figure shows how far there is to go in education about alcohol and how important it is not to take any knowledge for granted.

One thing you may not be aware of, that's important to pass on to your child, is quite how much difference there is between the effects of alcohol on a small person and on a large one. For instance, one unit of alcohol (one measure of a spirit, one glass of wine, or half a pint of beer) consumed over one hour will leave a $12^{1}/_{2}$-stone man with a blood alcohol concentration of 4 milligrams, but a woman weighing $8^{1}/_{2}$ stone drinking the same amount will have a blood alcohol concentration of 21 milligrams. A person's sex, weight, and speed of drinking will all affect this figure. The higher the blood alcohol concentration, the more the brain is affected, the more the brain's responses are dulled and slowed, and co-ordination, reaction and thought become more difficult and less sharp.

This will affect them whether they're trying to cross a road afterwards, or pull away from an over-attentive admirer at a party, or go for a swim, or climb a wall or tree afterwards – and the effects could lead to a fatal accident. But it will also affect them if they're trying to wash the dishes, chop an onion or mow the lawn. Accidents and upsets are all the more likely.

THE LEGAL POSITION

It's also worth you knowing exactly what the law says about children and alcohol:

- Up to the age of 5 it is illegal to give a child an alcoholic drink except under medical supervision, in cases of sickness or emergency.

- Up to the age of 14, no child is allowed into the bar of licensed premises.

- Up to the age of 18, no child can be sold alcohol at a bar and no child can work in a bar. However, 16 and 17-year-olds are allowed to buy beer, cider, sherry and port with meals in dining areas – eating areas without bars in them.

ADVICE FOR PARENTS

The charity Alcohol Concern has a ten-point advice plan for parents. This is:

1. Explain the facts about alcohol and the content of different types of drinks clearly (we've heard of young girls getting drunk on vermouth which they'd seen advertised on the telly and which they didn't think was 'real' alcohol).

2. Don't think you have to introduce your children to drink at a certain age. Wait until the young person asks for it.

3. Never leave alcoholic drinks lying around if young children are unsupervised.

4. Encourage children to eat when they have alcohol – they will not get drunk so easily.

5. Discuss social drinking and the right of choice to drink or not to drink. Discourage the idea that alcohol is an essential accompaniment for all pleasurable occasions and that drinking is 'grown up'.

6. Explain that alcohol is a major cause of accidents. Tell children they should never mix drink with risky activities such as swimming, climbing trees, or riding a bicycle or motor cycle.

7. Make sure they know the law.

8. Underline the dangers of drinking and driving.

9. Make an agreement with your child never to accept a lift with someone who has been drinking. Offer to pay for a taxi or arrange to collect her.

10. Young people learn by example. Ensure that you and your friends set an example by drinking sensibly.

As we've said, it's a wider and more complex message than just saying no, but it is a clear message nevertheless. All we are saying to them is be careful, be reasonable, and be safe.

SMOKING

For most parents this is a more clear cut issue, and rightly so. While most sensible parents will not object to their children drinking alcohol in moderation as part of a normal social life at least when they reach their mid teens, all parents with the welfare of their children in mind should strongly discourage them from smoking – even if mum and dad smoke themselves. Tar and nicotine do their young lungs no favours, and as we've already mentioned, the younger children start smoking regularly, the higher the chances are that they will die prematurely.

In the same way as alcohol abuse is seen as something grown-up and daring, smoking has at least an equal status. So many youngsters think they're being outrageous and independent by taking illicit puffs in the toilets at school, or while they're waiting in the bus queue.

In recent years some figures show a drop in the numbers of children who are taking up smoking – maybe the health messages are getting across. But the figures are still far too high.

It's not too early to talk to your children about smoking and health.

In a recent survey of 11 to 14-year-old smokers:

37% said they started smoking before they were 11.

34% said they smoked between 6 and 40 cigarettes per week.

17% said they smoked between 41 and 70 cigarettes per week.

15% said they smoked over 71 cigarettes per week

So how do children this age manage to get hold of so many cigarettes? They may be taking them from you if you smoke – so keep an eye on how many you have left in your opened packets and how many unopened packets you have in your home. Otherwise they may be cadging them from other children or their friends may be handing them out. Of course they may be buying packets themselves. Nearly 90% of regular smokers between the ages of 11 and 16 claim they buy cigarettes from shops. If you find evidence of this there are several questions you should be asking – one is, do your children have too much money to spend? If the answer is 'No', and if you're puzzled as to where the money came from or conversely where the cigarettes came from, it's worth pursuing that line of inquiry.

Another question worth asking is, 'Who, if anyone, has been selling your children cigarettes?'. The law on this question states clearly that it is illegal to sell cigarettes to children under 16. But it is estimated that 11 to 16-year-olds buy up to £90 million worth a year.

It's important for you to know that there is scientific proof that children who smoke are more susceptible to coughs and chest illnesses than those who don't. And that's just an immediate effect – the long-term effects, if it becomes a habit and they never give up, can be fatal. You may find out your child smokes by finding cigarettes in her pockets, by smelling tobacco smoke on her breath, her hair, or in her clothes (though the latter two may just mean she's been in the company of smokers) or because you spot her by chance. She may even feel she can smoke in front of you as a way of challenging your authority or maybe because you or your partner smoke. Whichever way you find out, and even if you receive no indication at all that she is a smoker or may be one in the future, the health message is one you should never be afraid to bring up and discuss with her. As we and anyone else in the medical profession will tell you, prevention is better than cure.

SOLVENT ABUSE

This is another important area – but one which might well be new to us as parents. We may have been as guilty as anyone else of having the occasional illicit fag or half of cider when we were growing up, but it's unlikely that today's parents will have been tempted to sniff glue out of an old crisp packet or nail varnish out of its bottle. It didn't really occur to us.

But it is occurring to youngsters these days – and the effects can be much more immediate and frightening than those of cigarette smoking.

In fact some experts believe that it is because many adults don't understand solvent abuse and at the same time strongly disapprove of it that children find it attractive. It is an excellent weapon in the 'generation war' because it is 'exclusive' to young people.

Sometimes it seems as if solvent abuse isn't taken as seriously as other drug abuse. There are many inquest reports in the papers of course, when young abusers have died as a result of their 'hobby', but there doesn't seem to be the same shock, horror about solvent abuse as there is about cocaine, heroin, and crack. But a recent survey of 3,000 secondary school pupils, carried out by the British Journal of Addiction, revealed that more children had tried solvents than any other single drug. And more children used solvents every day than any other single drug.

The same survey also showed that there is a rising trend of solvent abuse among girls and that the average age at which solvents and other drugs were first used was under 13, although most anti-drug information seems to focus on slightly older children. Surveys generally tend to suggest that between 7 and 10% of the secondary school age population has tried solvents. These are most definitely figures to bear in mind.

Because this is unlikely to have been something we experienced when we were children and because that fact in itself can make this form of abuse attractive to children, it's very important that we know exactly why youngsters sniff products, what happens when they do, why it is dangerous and what the signs are to look out for which show our children are abusing solvents.

The most common products to watch for are, of course, solvent based adhesives – brands such as Evo-stik. We list at the back of the book products which can be used in this way and which are commonly found in ordinary households. If you're not sure if a product is 'sniffable' you could ring the manufacturers and check, or ring one of the voluntary organisations listed at the back of this book which deal with this problem. Also watch out for any liquid marked 'highly flammable' or 'highly inflammable' or which contains 1,1,1-trichloroethane, methylene chloride, dichloromethane, or methylene dichloride. Not all of these items can be abused but if you have reason to suspect your child may be involved, they are worth investigating further or keeping an eye on.

'Sniffers' are often put into three categories. There is the experimenter, which accounts for the largest proportion. They will not continue with it for long. About 10% are thought to fit into the next category, which is regular users. They will carry on for a few months, often sniffing in groups. The smallest category is the habitual, long-term user.

Re-solv, one of the groups which works to prevent solvent abuse, says many youngsters are introduced to experimental solvent misuse by groups of friends but there are no general rules about which children will become abusers. Boredom, curiosity, and peer group pressure are some of the causes. Some studies show there are no social class barriers. But the dependent, long-term users and those who abuse by themselves and not as part of a group will inevitably have pre-existing social or emotional problems, in most cases to do with their family situation.

THE FACTS

Substances are usually inhaled from a small paper or plastic bag, such as a crisp packet, from a saturated rag, or by the direct spraying of an aerosol product into the mouth. Sometimes to enhance the effect a large plastic bag is placed over the abuser's head and sometimes the substance is heated first for the same purpose. Occasionally the substance is drunk – petrol or butane gas for example – and then it is usually mixed in a carbonated drink such as Coca Cola or lemonade, according to Re-solv.

The effects are almost immediate. Mild intoxication is achieved within a few minutes and can last up to half an hour. The user can experience hallucinations. By continually sniffing, an expert user can maintain the state of intoxication for up to 12 hours.

A lot of the dangers with glue sniffing result from the methods of use and from the circumstances in which the sniffing is carried out. If it's used in a dangerous place there is a risk of accidents occurring while the sniffer is intoxicated. If large plastic bags are placed over the head or face there's an increased danger of suffocation. If aerosols or compressed gases are sprayed directly into the mouth, adds Re-solv, the resulting sudden cooling of the tissues may cause a production of fluid which can block airways and cause suffocation in this way. There is also the possibility of sudden sniffing death as a result of aerosol or butane misuse followed by exertion.

For the experimental user the biggest dangers are from accidents when under the influence, and misuse of substances more dangerous than the usual glue. The longer term the user, the more the risks to health arising from continued use and, more generally, as a result of being more and more alienated from family and school. Accidents can result from the confusion, disorientation, risk-taking and aggression which can occur. Fits and unconsciousness, and vomiting which can cause suffocation when victims are in this sort of state, have all been known to result from solvent abuse.

Aerosols and volatile substances are more dangerous in themselves than sniffing glue. Some solvents can lead to anaemia and leukaemia, brain damage, liver and kidney damage, and heart failure, but as we've already said, these are not the most common hazards.

There have been relatively few deaths resulting from plain, ordinary, glue sniffing from a small bag. The important point therefore, as well as trying to stop them abusing in the first place, is to stop your child going any further and experimenting with other substances. It's important not to over-react and alienate your child, but to try to understand. In our communication chapter we will go into how to deal with finding out that your child is abusing solvents or other drugs and how to warn her of the risks. You can only do this if you know whether your child is abusing solvents and which signs to look for. These include:

- Traces or smells of glue or solvents on clothes or breath.

- A drowsy, vacant or glazed expression

- Unsteadiness

- Slurred speech or other signs similar to drunkenness.

Other indications are:

- Redness around the mouth and nose

- Blood-shot eyes

- Uncontrolled or excessive giggling and rowdy or silly behaviour.

In the longer term there can be:

- Secretive behaviour

- Irritability and restlessness

- Forgetfulness and loss of concentration

- Weight loss and depression.

Remember, solvents are very easily available and very cheap. It is not illegal to possess them, only to sell to people if there is reasonable cause to believe they intend to abuse them. If you fear your child is sniffing regularly, you must seek advice from experts and counsellors. This is too big a topic for you to deal with by yourself.

OTHER DRUG ABUSE

This is many parents' greatest fear, but again to a great degree it is a fear of the unknown. They are quite correct to be concerned – drug takers are not necessarily the gaunt, dishevelled youths which many automatically think of. Children from 'respectable' homes might also abuse drugs. Children from all classes and all groups in society have to face the pains of growing up and this may be one aspect of trying to cope or of making a display of independence and adulthood.

The facts about drug abuse are a lot less hysterical and sensational than the headlines about it would suggest. Children are far more likely to be in touch with illegal substances through their friends and companions than through seedy drug pushers in dirty macs. The chances are they will experiment, as all children like to experiment in anything new, and then grow out of it, maybe realising they'd rather spend their cash and time on other pursuits.

Just as an under-age drinker who's sneaked a half pint of lager won't necessarily turn into an alcoholic, so a youngster experimenting with glue or cannabis won't necessarily turn into a 'druggie' or a heroin addict. But it's as well to know as much as you can about the drugs they might come across, to arm yourself with information your children can respect and appreciate.

HEROIN

Heroin is derived from the opium poppy. It's also known as 'smack', 'H', 'skag', and 'junk'. It is the best known and most commonly abused of all opiate drugs, a category which includes opium, morphine, codeine, and synthetic opiate-type drugs such as methadone and pethidine. It produces pleasurable intoxication without making the individual feel 'drunk and incapable'.

It is mainly imported illegally, mixed with similar-looking white powders such as glucose, then divided into small quantities and sold usually wrapped in paper or in a small bag. The powder mixture can be grey, pink, or brown, as well as white. Most people still think of heroin as being dissolved in water and injected, but it can also be sniffed or smoked. Smoking it involves heating it on a piece of foil or a spoon and breathing in the fumes, often through a small tube. This is called 'chasing the dragon'. These two methods are now more widespread than injecting. The drug is addictive no matter which way it is taken, but it is a fact that most young people experimenting with heroin today will never become regular users. Addiction is more likely, says the Institute for the Study of Drug Dependence, if the young person has a disturbed or unhappy family background or psychological problems.

It is mainly a psychological need which leads to dependence on heroin. When the drug is taken frequently, bodies will develop a tolerance to its effects and will need more in order to get the effects they want. Eventually they may need to take the drug just to feel 'normal' and to prevent the appearance of withdrawal symptoms – a sign of physical as well as psychological dependence.

Injecting, which gives a stronger immediate 'high', is the most dangerous method of taking any drug. This raises the danger of overdosing and of introducing damaging bacteria, viruses, or powder into the blood stream. There is, of course, the danger of AIDS as the HIV virus can be contracted if a needle is shared with a person who is carrying the virus. Hepatitis can also be caught this way. Unsterile and dirty equipment can also lead to abscesses.

CANNABIS

This is also known as 'dope' and 'pot' and is a green and brown mixture of shredded leaves from the cannabis plant or a brown, solid, resin which must be heated and crumbled before use. In both cases it is usually smoked, often combined with tobacco, but it can also be mixed with food or brewed into a 'tea'. Some people may feel they need to take the drug to relax. This is the most commonly misused controlled drug in Britain.

COCAINE

Also called 'Coke', this is a white powder, usually sniffed. This is a more expensive drug. The derivative Crack, which is getting more and more publicity these days, is smoked and is available in small enough quantities for young people to be able to afford it.

But the cheap price is deceptive because the effects don't last long and some users find they can't stick to small doses. 'Rocks' of crack vary in size but they're roughly the size of a raisin and white in colour.

AMPHETAMINES

Also called 'uppers' or 'speed'. This is obtained in white powder form which is usually sniffed like Cocaine. After cannabis this is probably the second most commonly used illicit drug in this country. Users quickly establish a tolerance and so require ever-increasing doses. Withdrawal symptoms include feelings of tiredness, hunger, and depression. Purity levels tend to be very low – a large amount of other substances tend to be mixed in with the drug, which can be dangerous, particularly if it's injected.

ECSTASY

This is a hallucinogenic amphetamine, which has also had a lot of publicity recently. It is a drug which makes the user feel 'high'. It has psychedelic properties. It comes in pink, white, and yellow tablets, the size of pain killers.

BARBITURATES

These are known as 'downers' or 'barbs'. They come in different coloured capsules with street names which reflect the colour of the capsule such as 'reds' and 'blues. They are extremely addictive and easy to overdose on, particularly in conjunction with alcohol. Barbiturate injection is possibly the most dangerous form of drug abuse, with a high risk of overdose and physical injury. They are probably less available since they were declared 'controlled drugs' under the Misuse of Drugs Act, since Heroin became more cheaply available and since the non-medical use of tranquillisers became more popular.

TRANQUILLISERS

Obtained from medical supplies by theft or fraud, these can lead to dependence and unpleasant withdrawal symptoms. It's important for parents to realise that these are now 'street' drugs as much as any other drug which is abused, and they are easier to obtain. If you have them in the house, keep them locked away, and if you suspect your child may be abusing drugs, keep a close eye on the levels in your containers.

HALLUCINOGENS

These include LSD, or 'acid', and magic mushrooms. The main dangers are psychological rather than physical. But poisonous fungi can be picked by accident by drug users thinking they are collecting 'magic' mushrooms and these can be fatal. LSD is a transparent liquid blotted on to paper. Abusers then suck the paper which is impregnated with the drug.

AND REMEMBER

Some 'over-the-counter' drugs available from chemists without prescription can also be abused. If taken in large enough quantities they can give a 'high'. These include cough medicines containing opiates, travel sickness medicines, and decongestants containing antihistamines and nasal decongestants based on ephedrine or pseudoephedrine.

Also easily available are volatile nitrites sold in little bottles in nightclubs and elsewhere under trade names such as Liquid Gold, which intoxicate when they are sniffed.

Hopefully this list will help you to identify any drugs your child may be trying. The risks are often in the effects the drugs have in removing inhibitions and clouding judgement. Accidents are more easily caused and the drug misuser is more likely to find herself in a dangerous situation or a situation she cannot control, and would have avoided had she been 100% in control of her thoughts and actions.

Add to this the fact that sometimes the substances mixed in with the drugs and sometimes the drugs themselves can harm their health, and the fact that drug taking in these forms is illegal and so your children are committing crimes, and drug-taking does become very serious indeed. It's expensive, too – and that, at its worst, can lead to other criminal activity to pay for it. The other factor to remember is that a child regularly taking drugs is a child not coming to terms with life, a child not coping with life without artificial stimulants, which is something all parents have a responsibility to tackle.

Chapter Nine
COMMUNICATING WITH YOUR 10-14 YEAR OLD

DON'T 'JUST SAY NO'

Way back near the beginning of this book we gave you what we suggested was your best response if you saw your child approaching something dangerous and about to injure herself. That response was one word long. The word was 'No'.

But that will not do any longer – in fact, it won't have been sufficient for many years. Your child has grown a great deal, has progressed, is making her way towards adulthood and independence. She has a point of view, she has rights, she has a life of her own. And you must respect her rights and her point of view and allow her to live her own life.

That's not to say you must agree with what she says all the time. You are the adult and she is the child and you have a much better idea of what she must keep herself safe from and what the dangers are that she might face. She still needs your guidance and your support. But you must discuss what she wants and what she feels is right. And when necessary, you must be prepared to compromise, even if you know you'll never have a moment's peace of mind until she's safely back home again. If you are reasonable in your dealings with her she should begin to feel that your knowledge and views on subjects that are still mysterious to her, such as glue sniffing and drinking pints, may be worthwhile and relevant.

IT'S NOT TOO LATE

Communicating generally will be difficult at this stage in your relationship with your child if you haven't already laid the foundations for a firm, trusting relationship between you. But even if your relationship hasn't always run smoothly and you feel there's been too much of a distance between you, don't feel it's too late to change.

You can try to make up for lost time if you approach things in the right way starting from now. Show an interest; don't jump to conclusions; don't patronise. Respect your child as an individual – treat your 10 to 14-year-old as you would any other person, giving her a sense of worth. Any step-parent entering an almost grown-up family will tell you that it isn't always easy building a relationship with a child this age which doesn't have the firm foundations they'd like, but it is still worth putting your time and your energy into it. You'll both get so much more out of it.

PEER GROUP INFLUENCE

The 'Are they ready?' question we've mentioned before will still be looming large. Of course now it will relate to new areas: 'Are they ready to go to the disco?', 'Are they ready to do a paper round early in the morning when it's still dark?', 'Are they ready to go shopping in town by themselves?'. And now there is slightly more to consider in your answers. Very interesting research by the Scottish Health Education Group tells us why. The Group has published a chart which shows the relative importance of different influences on children according to age groups. For the 6 to 10 age group parents have by far the most influence on children. Their influence is described as 'medium to high'. Second to parents in the influence stakes comes a group described as 'legitimate sources of authority' – such as teachers in schools – and they are of 'medium importance'. Peer group influence is of 'low importance'.

But for the 10 to 14-year old age group, the picture is very different. Now peer group influence is the only one in the 'medium to high' category; down to 'medium' comes parental influence, and legitimate sources of authority have only a low level of influence – the same level, in fact, as the children said they were influenced by their own ideas. It's also interesting to learn how these categories change for older children. For 14s to 17s, children say they influence themselves and their friends influence them the most, and for the over-17s by far the most influential group are the young people themselves on themselves.

From this we can gather that it is not until they're older than the children we cover in this book that their own opinions are formulated individually, often without outside help, and they have confidence in them. They are still highly influenced by those round them, and for 10-14s, the biggest influence is that of other children. This means the biggest influence is not necessarily a healthy one or a well-informed one. So when our children start asking our permission to do things we're not sure about and when we start asking ourselves, 'Are they ready?' there is this to take into account, too. Our children may be asking for permission to do things which they've been persuaded by their friends are good to do. They will not understand the risks, they may not understand why we pause when other mothers have given their permission or when their friends don't even need to ask permission from their mothers. They just go ahead and do it.

THE FIGHT FOR INDEPENDENCE

However much you explain, argue and negotiate, however much time and care you put into your relationship with them, this is a time in their lives when they will be demanding that you let them do things, they will be continually trying to demonstrate to you that they are growing up and they are independent. And sometimes when you say they can't do something or they shouldn't do it, they will go ahead and do it anyway, even if it's something as simple as picking up a hot dish from the oven using only a tea towel as protection and burning themselves in the process. Of course, their disobedience may revolve around something much more serious.

Sometimes they may come to grief, sometimes they won't, but you'll find out what they've been doing and you may be furious. Sometimes you'll feel your children are the worst in the world and that you are the most persecuted parents. But don't forget, making that sort of challenge to parents' authority is part of adolescence, is part of growing up. In order for your child to grow up she has to find out how different she is from her parents. She has to find out who she is and what she can do and what kind of place the world is. That is something she has to do partly by herself. She will be establishing for herself, through trial and error, what she can do and what she can't.

So it's natural she may go too far and venture into something she can't cope with. At which point the relationship of trust you have hopefully built up with her should allow her to come and tell you about it so you can help her understand and come to terms with what she's done and handle the situation for herself.

REMEMBERING THE MESSAGES

Having said this, it would be less stressful and less dangerous for all concerned if she learnt the lessons you want to teach her well enough to be able to recognise dangerous situations and keep her distance, or for her to be able to limit the damage that may be caused. She may have gone out with the group you'd told her you were worried about her mixing with, and found herself in the middle of a bunch of their friends all taking drugs. She may have found that her only way out was to leave and try to get home by herself – and that meant waiting by herself at a darkened bus stop. But if she has remembered the lessons you've taught her, at least she'll know not to accept lifts from seemingly friendly passing motorists; at least she'll know to keep alert and keep an eye out for anyone who spells danger; and if she's very frightened after her experiences of the evening, at least she'll know to give you a ring so you can help her out.

INTO THE TEENS

So how best do you communicate? Remember, this may not be an easy time, especially as your child moves into her early and mid-teens. She won't want to do what you say all the time, especially if you have a tendency to be over-protective. She may be continually challenging you and reacting aggressively to what you say. There may be a moodiness and a distancing separating your child from you – this may be particularly true of girls – when she doesn't have the verbal skills to discuss what she wants to with you and she feels embarrassed and awkward anyway, so she cuts you off and feels that you don't understand. Remember, too, her hormones will be doing all sorts of things inside her body which will be affecting her behaviour, so her behaviour does make sense, even if that sometimes doesn't make it easier to bear.

Communication is never a one-way process. It's always about listening to each other. And if your child is behaving in that 'difficult' way, there's obviously a lot troubling her and a lot she might be discussing with you if she felt she could. You can't force children to talk but you can make yourself obviously available, to make it easier for them if they want to.

TOGETHERNESS

Your child may have worries about issues you won't have thought she was ready to know about yet. She may have questions about subjects you thought you'd already discussed with her and you'd all agreed on, which she just hasn't felt she can talk to you about. It will greatly help her keep safe at this stage in her life, as well as in the earlier stages, if you can *tackle together* what frightens her and what she sees as life's dangers and life's problems. It makes the message so much clearer if she brings up the topic of discussion, if it's clearly something that interests her and she wants to talk it over with you. It's then harder for her to pretend she's not interested or that she thinks you're too out of touch and out of date to know what you're talking about. It's also harder for you to start preaching and lecturing. You must also ask her point of view and the points of view she has heard from her friends and from others – maybe on the television or the radio or in school breaks.

In general we don't communicate as families as much as we used too. There's rarely a set-up which involves a big meal all together once a day for the whole family in today's modern households. There are all sorts of reasons for this – television is the main one which limits conversation, no doubt, but shift work, and other changing work patterns such as more women going out to work, play their part as well. So does the general pace of life – everyone seems to be rushing around much more these days with scarcely time to wolf down a cheese sandwich at tea time, let alone sit and eat and chat with plenty of time to enjoy both.

At one time in many households there was a chance for everyone to raise subjects they wanted, and discuss the issues that concerned them (even if the system didn't always work like that if, say, everyone was too scared of dad to mention anything remotely out of order or fun). But the chance of a discussion together was almost institutionalised, part of the daily routine.

MAKING TIME TO TALK

That's no longer true for most families, so it's important we try to make up for this with new routines which will mean everyone will at least have the chance, even if they don't take it up, to have their say and talk about what concerns them. With younger children that might happen at bedtime, when you read them a bedtime story or go to tuck them in. With older children it could happen when you both have a warm drink before bed, or when they come home from school, or if you go on an outing, maybe to the swimming baths, together. This doesn't have to be a compulsory chat every single day, but you should make efforts to fit one in several times a week.

It shouldn't be an inquisition. It should be a time to ask, 'How was your day?', 'What's happening tomorrow?', 'Did you see that girl who was rude to you at school the other day?', 'Have you had any more run-ins with your maths teacher?', 'What happened to your friend who was told off for wearing make-up in class?', 'How do you feel about that boy who was expelled for playing truant? Did he get into any trouble when he should have been at school?'. Discuss the subjects that come along with a real interest in what your child has to say; don't just see them as a chance to give your two pennyworth an airing. Help your child to make her own judgements about events and situations; don't do it for her. Ask, 'And what did you think when Jimmy hurled his geography book across the classroom?' Let her put her viewpoint across.

WATCH FOR THE OPPORTUNITIES

If there's something on your child's mind that she wants to tell you but doesn't and the opportunity never arises because the phone's always ringing or you're always busy fitting the housework in after a busy day at work, it might be too late. You've missed an opportunity to hear something very important to her.

If that something is quite serious but she's been warned not to tell her parents – if she's been or is being sexually abused, for example, or if she's being very badly bullied at school – she may be in two minds whether to tell you in any case. That's why it is so important not to miss the vital moment – the moment you do something or say something which tells your child she will get an understanding reception; that you won't blame her or fly off in a dreadful temper proclaiming how you're going to go and sort out whoever has been upsetting or assaulting her. She needs to be sure you will listen to what she wants you to do, before you announce any decision you've come to. Those decisions should be joint decisions – even if you have to use all the parental influence in your power to convince her that your course of actions is the correct one. She'll have to have a lot of faith in you to break the confidence she's promised to keep, and to know that you'll react in a way she can trust and that won't embarrass her or make the problem worse. If you then interrupt this chat to watch your favourite television programme you may well have missed the vital moment. You must learn to read your child, not to be impatient with her if she's not forthcoming for a while, but give her a chance to work out how best to express herself. And give her the time to do it.

By watching your child's reactions you should gather how best to communicate. It may be that children at the earlier end of this age group still find it easier to talk when you're not looking each other in the eye. It may flow better when you're both involved in a task that's not taking up too much of your attention for you to concentrate on what the other is saying. And if your child's feeling greatly embarrassed or you think you both need a breather you could change topics to your task at hand before returning to your proper chat. This might help your child realise, too, that something she was worried about isn't such an enormous problem – there are other things in life, too.

WHEN THINGS GET SERIOUS

As your child gets older there may need to be more of a structure, especially if the casual, daily chats aren't working. If your child seems too alienated to confide in you and too rebellious to take in what you want to say to her, you may need to exert your authority more obviously and say something like, 'I think we should have a talk'. This is the case, as well, if you've heard your child is getting involved in an activity you don't approve of, or if you're worried about one aspect of her life in particular.

Even if you can communicate easily and almost casually, and even if both of you enjoy your chats, we're not trying to suggest that you are casual and 'laid back' about important topics. Children will be hearing from plenty of sources the young, trendy attitude towards drugs, alcohol and cigarettes without you joining in in that vein. Even if you don't have strong views on, say, smoking cannabis, you should be aware how much more likely it is your child will have an accident or get into trouble if she indulges. And that's to say nothing about the fact that she's committing an illegal act and that will have a big effect on her future if she's caught.

So sound adult, and sound confident and sure of yourself. That's partly why it's so important to know the facts. You need to be able to answer your children's questions. Even on such a structured occasion, communication is still a two-way process. And don't forget our rules for 'true communication'. If your child says, 'I'm worried about school,' don't launch into a major nagging session about how she should be doing more homework. She may be worried about a particular teacher, other children, or any other aspect of school life. With gentle questioning, you can help her tell you.

MAKE USE OF YOUR OPPORTUNITIES

There's always a danger that if you bring up a subject for discussion, your child will feel you're 'getting at her', or she may feel embarrassed and awkward that it's being brought up so obviously and not in any context – she'll feel it's obviously aimed at her and you'll all be studying her for her reaction. There are ways round that: If you're all watching television together and something shocking appears on the screen, don't turn over, unless it's something you seriously disapprove of her seeing. If it's a violent scene in a cop show, it's a good opportunity to discuss the fact that most people hit as hard as they appear to be on screen won't be able to fight back in the way that actors manage it – they'd be out for the count. If it's a news report about deaths from drug abuse, or a prominent figure who's been banned from driving after being caught behind the wheel under the influence, or a young girl who's abandoned her baby in a plastic bag on the steps of a hospital, it's a good time to discuss any of those issues together as a family, examining what's happened and why it's happened, whether you can understand it, whether it's right or wrong.

If your daughter hears you saying, 'How terrible, that poor girl didn't feel she could tell her mum and dad she was pregnant', she may learn from that that you acknowledge that mistakes can happen and if the worst happened in the future she could come to you. But you can teach other lessons from the same news item – about the responsibilities on one so young, about the precautions that could have been taken, about the guilt she will unquestionably feel. And if your son, who's already enjoying a few illicit cans that his friend's older brother has brought from the local off licence and feeling very grown up about it, hears you discussing how terrible it is that a man who should know better has put lives at risk by driving under the influence of drink, and hears you outlining the awful consequences that could have resulted, he may learn from that that not all drinking is adult, clever behaviour, that alcohol can be abused with consequences that can stay with you forever.

The telly doesn't have to be the only focus of attention. There may be a grisly report in newspapers or magazines which you can talk about. By this stage there's little to be gained by shielding your children from real life pain, tragedy and grief. There's no point in holding back on the details of the worst effects of drug abuse or of taking a lift with a stranger. You don't want to be gory and you don't want to terrify your children. But you do want them to know enough to help them make decisions about how to react to situations. If your child is being approached by a stranger on a dark night and there's no one to turn to for help, depriving her of information won't help her scream or run rather than stand frozen to the spot. But she also doesn't want to be so terrified of all strangers that she won't accept help from someone trying to protect her, believing that, unquestionably, he will want to assault her or steal from her too.

You could come home and mention something you've just seen on the street outside – maybe joy riders who didn't know what they were doing and nearly ploughed into a little girl and her mum, or a pickpocket who raced down the street after being spotted but was caught in the end, or a teenager too busy chatting to her friend to notice the traffic, who almost got run over. As we've said before, an illustration always helps get any message across, and with older children it's always likely to be an illustration of an incident that happened to someone else which they can relate to, and really understand, the implications of which should hit home.

ADULT DISCUSSIONS

So if neither you nor your partner smoke and you have a friend round who does and you're talking to him or her about it and if they regret starting, don't exclude your child. There's nothing wrong with letting a 10 to 14-year-old take part in adult discussions. She'll have questions she wants to ask, too. She may want to ask your friend whether he felt healthier before it all began. Your friend might talk about the money he wished he'd saved or how good he was at swimming/football/disco dancing when he was younger and how much stamina he had in his days before tobacco. He might mention how much whiter his teeth used to be and how his complexion seemed fresher before and how his friends sometimes have a go at him for smelling of cigarette smoke all the time. All these messages should appeal to your child – she will be able to relate directly to all the anti-smoking messages. (In fact, children can be fearsome health campaigners!) She should be encouraged to join in the conversation. You could ask her, 'What do you think?' or 'Do you know anyone who smokes?' or 'Has anyone offered you a cigarette?'.

If your child has smoked, she may feel safer discussing the subject with someone from outside the immediate family circle present, as she may decide you wouldn't have brought the subject up in front of an outsider if you were about to let rip and shout and scream at her. The fact that a smoker is present, as someone else who's succumbed to the temptation, may make her feel she can admit she has tried a cigarette and that she can discuss with you why she did, and what she thinks about all the other issued to do with smoking that have been raised.

LETTING GO

In fact you may find your child prefers to confide in others about some areas of her life. She may choose a teacher, a family friend, a neighbour. You shouldn't take this as an insult – you should be proud that your child is grown up enough to make that sort of decision for herself, to decide whom she can turn to and whom she can trust. She's entitled to her privacy just as you are, and if you create the right atmosphere and if you give her the time she deserves, she may well tell you in her own time. You shouldn't be competitive with other adults for your child's attention and affection – you should have a special relationship with her in any case which will be greater and more powerful than any that another adult has, if you insist on seeing it in power terms. And you should certainly not put any pressure on those other adults to break your child's confidences. If they're worried about the information that's been entrusted to them and think your child's safety is in danger, they're bound to tell you in any case, and discuss with you what action to take and how best to approach your child. They won't want the burden of the whole future well-being and security of your child on their shoulders. It doesn't belong there. The important point here is that your child should have responsible adults she can trust. In one particular area, through no one's fault, she may decide that that person will not be you. But don't be threatened by it – even if the person chosen is a step-parent or estranged partner. Your child may simply be seeking out the opinions of other adults. She may be thinking, 'I know mum feels like this – do all women feel like this?'.

Remember, you don't own your child. Your child will need other adults besides you. She'll need her own space sometimes.

TELL THE TRUTH

Meanwhile when the two of you do talk together, whatever the issue is that's being discussed, it's important that you tell her the truth. It's one thing not hiding any facts from her, but it's another exaggerating and distorting those facts.

So don't tell her all drugs are evil while happily feeding yourself with as many (on prescription, of course) as you can lay your hands on. The Institute for the Study of Drug Dependence says parents should set an example and not use drugs indiscriminately. From the time their children are quite young, they should stress that the taking of any drug or medicine has a serious purpose. This, says the Institute, gives children a respect for drugs and establishes the whole area as a subject for discussion.

And don't tell them all alcohol is evil while having your daily tipple. Children object strongly to not being taken seriously and not being treated like sensible individuals who can spot contradictions of that sort as easily as they unscrew the lid of a bottle of cider.

When you're discussing dangers with your child, it's important that you tell her the whole story about whatever it is you're talking about. Don't just say, 'Don't hitchhike', full stop, end of discussion, end of debate, 'And I don't want the word mentioned again in this house.' Explain your reasons for not approving of the practice. But also point out why so many people do it. Your child is bound to see plenty of hitchhikers around if she ever travels outside the town or village you live in, and they won't all look stupid and ignorant. They certainly won't look as if a curse has fallen on them because they're doing something forbidden, and they won't look as if they've just been attacked or abused.

There's nothing wrong with explaining why many people do hitchhike, underlining, of course, that they will be older than your children are. It is a free method of transport and that in itself can be very attractive to a lot of people. If the positive side of hitchhiking hasn't been spelt out to your child by you – if you haven't shown that you've looked at every side and come down against it although you are aware of the benefits – your child will be more inclined to be influenced by a friend who suddenly brings this great new attraction to mind. It's quite a persuasive argument – if we hitch we can afford to buy that new record or that eye shadow we saw the other day – but it's less persuasive if she's heard it before but decided her own safety is more important.

Tell the truth, also, when you're discussing drug abuse. If you only tell your child that drug addicts are the scourge of society, dirty and unwanted, she is hardly likely to confide in you if she hears of it, is offered some or has particular worries or queries about the subject. And if you respond to a question from her, 'Why do people take drugs?' by saying, 'Because they're bad and no good and don't know any better', that isn't going to help in the long term.

If your child is ever tempted, she may realise for the first time that her friends are right about one thing that you've never mentioned, so you obviously didn't know about it – that taking drugs can give them a feeling they've never felt before. Put bluntly, it can make them feel great.

There's no reason for you to miss out of any conversation you're having with your child about drug abuse, the fact that drug abusers enjoy it – at least to begin with. But then you can immediately put that into context by talking about addiction, about health risks, and about the safety risks of drug abuse. Far better that they hear it all in context than that they find out it can give them a high and accept this fact independently, giving it a bigger importance than the down side.

A REASONED ARGUMENT

Whatever it is you're discussing it's always worth showing your children that you have weighed up the pros and cons and have come down on one particular side – and that's the only sensible side to take. It's possible they'll hear the 'pros' from others in any case, notably from other youngsters daring them to have a go. But because there'll be strong influences urging them to do just that and putting forward an unsafe message, it's vital that you don't sound wishy-washy when you put your views across. You're not saying that you can see both points of view and that both points of view are acceptable. You are simply saying that there might be some immediate fun to come out of it but there might be frightening effects in the long term. It's not worth the risk.

Drug experts, to give just one example, say that if you say 'No' to your children without explaining reasons or discussing anything about the issue, they can react by escalating their drug usage from maybe a little glue sniffing into more dangerous new areas which they don't know about themselves. This is seen as unintentional provocation by parents, which should be avoided.

It's also interesting that some youngsters from cultures or from homes where drinking is banned turn to alcohol in a big way. Again the information they will have received will probably have been one-sided and, in addition, the issue will probably have been given too much prominence in the household, thereby arousing the curiosity of the children who are bound to hear alternative viewpoints and see other sides to the question of drinking alcohol in their day-to-day lives.

If you approach all these issues in a broad way, examining all sides and all arguments, the information your child hears from you won't conflict with what she's hearing from others, thereby undermining your case – unless, of course, the others are intentionally or unintentionally misleading her. It will correspond with it, but your child will hopefully come to a different conclusion and a different plan of action from that of others putting forward drugs as a 'good time'. However, you don't want to suggest that taking drugs is such good fun that her curiosity to try them out will get the better of her. That's like a magazine carrying dieting articles on losing 7lb in seven days alongside recipes for 'the best chocolate cake ever'. Don't confuse. Be direct, be straight, be firm.

'LOOK WHAT HAPPENED TO ME!'

It's worth pointing out, too, that we can't always do what's fun and what we want to do and never mind the consequences. Use as illustrations things that have happened in your child's life, occasions she sensibly held back when knowing it could be dangerous to go ahead. Or use things that happened in your youth, or to you recently. It will impress your child if you can show her you have personal experience of some of these safety issues, that you haven't just been reading books like this one which tell you what to do. Do you remember accepting a lift home from a man you didn't know because you thought your parents would tell you off if you got home late, only to find he was saying rude things to you or trying to touch you? Tell your children how you got out of that situation. Do you remember how you were so drunk one night that you fell down a steep flight of stairs, or you ruined your favourite dress or everyone laughed at you and never let you forget it, and you felt really ashamed at some of the things you'd said and done? Tell your children how hurt and mortified you felt.

A UNITED FRONT

None of these messages will be very strong if your partner is sending out different ones. If you're trying to tell your son about the dangers of drinking to excess and in the background your partner is showing off about how many pints he used to down when he was a lad, or if you're trying to tell your daughter about how to cope with men giving her too much attention while your partner is recounting tales of his success with women and how many hearts he broke, and whatever else besides, it won't help at all. Your child will be as confused and unconvinced as your toddler would be if her mum and dad were in turn telling her off for jumping off the sofa and congratulating her on being a big, brave girl.

IN THE EVENT

So what if you do find out your child has been doing something you thought you'd both agreed was dangerous and a bad idea? If you find out yourself – maybe by finding a box of cigarettes in her jacket pocket or some evidence of drug taking in her bedroom – it may well be that she wanted you to. Children are perfectly capable of hiding the fact that they smoke or that they use drugs for as long as they want to. They're pretty smart. Depending on how serious the matter is, she could be making a cry for help to you. She could feel she needs someone to help her sort herself out but she doesn't know whom to turn to. On the other hand it could be a cry for attention, especially if she has younger brothers and sisters. She may feel that you've left her to her own devices, that you see her as more able to look after herself. But she still needs care and attention. And that's exactly what you should give her. It might just be a sort of bravado – her way of telling you that she is running her own life now. That message is still one that needs to be discussed and talked through. She may be trying to tell you she's bored, or moving towards depression and in both cases you can help, and should try to help before her boredom leads her to more harmful activities or before her depression deepens.

Whatever she is trying to tell you, you will need to respond. Her actions will need a reaction from you that's caring and considered. Just as we should look at the reasons why our children climb too high on the climbing frame or accept sweets from strangers when we've told them not to, so we should look at why our children are risking their own health and safety at this stage in their lives.

Remember, by the time she gets to this age, your child will know more about the dangers around her and how to cope with them. Children aged 10 and 11 were the oldest covered by the University of Southampton research team we've mentioned before. By this age the children were scarcely mentioning the imaginary dangers such as ghosts and witches which were confusing their safety messages earlier in childhood. They could name far longer lists of dangerous people – including muggers, burglars, glue sniffers, vandals, and gangs; they could name far longer lists of potentially dangerous objects – sockets, bunsen burners, lighted cigarettes, wires, chemicals, medicines, tablets, toadstools; they could name far longer lists of dangerous places and situations – fighting, smoking, asking people for money, playing 'wheelies' on their bicycles, breaking in, building sites, taking drugs, even 'being stupid'. They were no longer confusing getting told off by mum, or getting into trouble with dad, with the real dangers around them.

By the age of 10, seven out of ten youngsters were still saying it was an adult's job to keep them safe, but by the age of 11, half were saying it was the job of the adults, and half were saying it was their job too. No doubt these figures change again for 12, 13 and 14-year-olds.

So our children seem to know much more about keeping safe. We can tell them that it is often braver and more grown up to say 'No' to things than it is to bow to pressure. We can tell them exactly where the dangers are and how they should avoid them. We can tell them what we like.

But still things can go wrong. We are not perfect parents – we can't hope to be. Our children aren't perfect either – we should not expect them to be. Dealing with your child who's been sniffing glue or getting drunk is all part of the communication process.

ALL ON THE SAME SIDE

The most important point to make here is that it's vital you don't over-react, however angry or alarmed you feel. Looking at things in one way, if your child's been taking cannabis, it's not a disaster. For a start it's highly unlikely she'll be jabbing heroin into her arm a week later. Take time to talk it through calmly, find out what your child is trying to prove, what she is trying to escape from. She maybe feeling inadequate, lonely, bored, or bullied. Find out whether she's unhappy at school. Make enquiries, talk to her teachers. Make a bigger effort to find out if anything's troubling her. She may be trying to avoid facing up to the underlying causes for her behaviour. She needs your help, not terrifying punishments. Often the shame of being caught doing something she knows you disapprove of so strongly, of breaking her part of the bargain she made with you, of letting you down, will be punishment enough. Never wash your hands of her. She's still your responsibility. She still needs your help. But never be afraid to seek outside help either. You might both need it. Your child will be making the transition to adulthood. That's never easy – it never has been for any generation. You'll remember it wasn't for you and it's not for your child either. As parents we can only do our best to help. And by helping them we are showing them the most important message of all, the message we need to communicate to them most of all – that we are all on the same side.

Chapter Ten
PARENTS AND STRESS

There's an image so often created in today's world of the perfect family, complete with perfect parents and perfect children. It's everywhere – on the sides of baby food packets and nappy packs, in television commercials for everything from cornflakes to cosmetics to washing powder. We see it on advertising hoardings in the street, on the pages of our newspapers and magazines, and perhaps we think it's also in the houses of our friends and neighbours. Everywhere we see babies who are always happy and gurgling, shiny haired children, pre-schoolers always saying the cutest things, teenagers making their own beds at home, and making their mark in the maths class and the football team at school, and perfect mums who always wash everything whiter. We're surrounded!

In fact we'll find these images everywhere apart from just one place – our homes. Because there really isn't a home in Britain that's trouble free, problem free, stress free.

We've already mentioned that we believe few new parents are properly prepared for the task they've taken on. No one is taught about parenting or trained in the skills that help us do as good a job of it as we are able. The only example we have to follow is the one we learned while we were growing up. In addition there is a great deal of pressure on young couples to have children. It's popularly seen as one of the key ways to become socially acceptable and to prove that we live contented, successful lives. We 'fit in' with what everyone expects of us when we announce a baby is on the way after finding the partner we want to spend our lives with. Childlessness is usually treated, by friends and family of the childless couple, with sympathy and sorrow rather than as an opportunity for the couple to have more time with each other and more time to enhance different, separate areas of their lives.

So some parents may have started the whole business without fully considering the implications. It will have been the 'done thing'.

Whether or not that is true, few new parents can be completely aware quite how difficult it is bringing up children – quite how much time and effort they need, quite how much they change your lives forever.

GOOD TIMES, BAD TIMES

That's not to say children are a burden. We can love them and we can love taking care of them, but we can do both of these things while still acknowledging that they do cause us worry and do take up a great deal of our energy. Every parent reading this will know that sudden horrifying moment when you look round expecting to see your child behaving beautifully next to you – you've only turned your back for a moment – but when you spin round you see her reaching for something dangerous or dashing towards another hazard. We've all experienced that terrible feeling when our heart seems to stop for a moment, that sudden surge of panic and dread. And there are the more long term anxieties. We fear our children are crying too much, aren't sleeping enough, may be ill, aren't using the potty soon enough, aren't eating enough, might not like nursery, might not like school, might not like big school, might get into trouble, might get in with the wrong crowd. Yes, we worry about our children. That's a fact which is natural and it's real.

STRESSES AND STRAINS

But our children aren't all we worry about. Our stress may come from elsewhere in our lives – our wallets, or our relationship with our partner for example. And it may be we are blaming our children for the stress we feel instead of looking for the real, underlying cause of it all. What's certainly true is that if there are financial problems in the family, if there are problems between husband and wife, having a child with all the extra responsibilities, the extra concern and the extra time that entails, is likely to add to the stresses which resulted from the original causes.

While accepting it's a fact of life that parents will feel stressed at some points, we also have to acknowledge that there comes a time when stress becomes a real problem – a problem with more effects than slightly raised blood pressure or the odd sleepless night. It becomes a problem which can upset and damage the whole family.

So when does stress, in itself, become a problem? Every individual has the capacity to cope with a particular amount of stress, so it's impossible to say what level is too high a level – you can't go and measure it on a machine at the doctor's surgery to see if everything's OK. You have to look at the effect it's having on your life. Ask yourself if you are continually feeling stressed, or are you confident that you are capable of handling the stress that you feel. Do you feel stressed all the time – do you have a feeling that everything is stressful, that one thing piles up on another? If it's your child causing you stress, are you able to escape from that, to go out for an evening leaving your child in capable hands, and relax? If it's your job causing you stress are you able to leave your problems at the office door or the factory gates, or do you bring your tension and your moods home with you every night?

HAVE A BREATHER

This is meant to be a book about child safety and well-being, so you may feel that these questions about stress are in the wrong book – shouldn't they be in a book about parental well-being instead? No. The truth is these two issues cannot be separated. To give your best to your child you have to be feeling good yourself. You have to allow yourself space away from your child – allow yourself time to think. It may be, especially if you're a single parent, that the only time this might be possible is soaking in a hot bath at the end of the day while your baby's asleep in her cot. It may be you can only afford a babysitter once a month. You may have more opportunity than this to have time for yourself, but whatever is the case, you shouldn't feel guilty about wanting and needing time to think these through, to think about what's worrying you and why, and then to look at your priorities. No one who goes out to work would dream of slogging away all day without a break for a meal or a cup of tea and a quick breather. Well, you've been working and concentrating hard too. You deserve one too.

The other problem to watch out for, apart from not giving yourself breathing spaces, is not having anyone to talk to. Isolation can bring a great deal of stress. Everyone feels better if they talk through their problems and their worries with someone else – why else would the Samaritans exist? If you're a parent on your own, or if your partner is rarely about and isn't attentive to your needs or your child's, and you haven't got friends and family to rely on as much as you'd like, the threat of isolation is a real one.

LET'S TALK IT OVER

Talking things over with someone gives you the opportunity to stop and ask yourself, 'Where is my stress coming from? What's the root cause? What can I do about this? How can I make sure I don't get too stressed by it?' This can help you work out answers to your problems and ways of coping with your difficulties for yourself. It can get what's happening in your life into perspective. It can help you see the good as well as the bad. If there's no one to talk to, if you don't confide your fears, if you don't give yourself time to think, the problems and the stresses can take over everything else. If that happens, there'll be no room in your over-anxious mind for enjoyment and relaxation – for enjoying your child, enjoying yourself and enjoying your own peace of mind.

When it comes to parenting, most people follow the example of their parents. After all, this will be just about the only information they'll have been given about how to do it. And situations and attitudes which bring stress can be passed down from generation to generation. This is another reason why communicating with other parents or others who can sympathise, who may have different experiences, who may be able to see things more objectively, is so useful.

If, for example, your child continually picks and plays with her food at the table, you may worry she's not eating enough and try to make her eat more. Mealtimes may start to become very stressful times. The dinner table can feel more like a battle ground. By stopping to think – and with help to put this into perspective – parents may start to say to themselves, 'Maybe she's eating a lot at school. Maybe she's getting her calorie intake another way - does she drink a lot of milk during the day? Maybe she is actually eating enough for her needs although she seems only to be picking at the food'.

Let's look at another example. If your child isn't doing well at school and that's really worrying you, it's very useful to ask yourself why it's worrying you so much. Could it be that you didn't perform so well in school yourself and that's why you want your child to succeed? Are you expecting your child to live the life you want her to lead, rather than the one she wants to lead and is suited to?

If you feel you can't cope with the amount you have to pack into the day – if you feel you haven't got the energy and the patience to clean the oven even though it's down on your list of things to do, ask yourself if you need to do it. The world won't collapse around you if you decide to leave it until you feel better, if you decide to prioritise and accept that you haven't got limitless energy, time and patience.

Whatever the reason for your stress, it's always worth asking yourself, 'Why am I so het up about this? Is this really the reason I'm worrying?' Often an outsider can help you answer both questions.

OTHER TYPES OF STRESS

It may be that your problem is a wider one than that. You may feel that you can't concentrate on anything; that you're arguing more with the people close to you; that maybe your alcohol intake's shooting up; that you're never unstressed – you're always worrying; that you're not sleeping at night and that perhaps you're not having many good times with your child; that you feel ill – maybe there's a cold you can't shake off or you're constantly having headaches – and the doctor can't see a medical reason for it. In this case, you may find yourself in a sort of vicious circle of stress. You feel so bad, it's hard to pinpoint where it all began, what the root causes are.

We've said before that children soak up the feelings around them. So you may be thinking, 'I wish the children would stop playing up. I wouldn't be so upset if they would behave themselves.' But it might be that the children's bad behaviour results from them feeling uncomfortable because they can sense everyone is on edge. That doesn't mean you should feel guilty, it doesn't mean you are 'to blame'. Neither of these attitudes will help at all. Anyone can understand how a mum with 3 children under 5, with poor housing conditions and a husband out of work, can feel too swamped by worry and stress to find time for herself to think up solutions. But that's exactly what she must do. Because the next matter we're going to deal with here is child abuse.

CHILD ABUSE - WHAT IS IT?

When most people read those two words 'child abuse' they think, we imagine, of child sexual abuse, or of the horrific stories about babies battered, neglected and left to die which we all hear about and read about. They think of abuse that is premeditated, planned and sadistic. But there are other forms of child abuse which are stress related.

When people are under a great deal of stress they will have less tolerance. This means they may deal with their children in a more aggressive way than they would otherwise. They may lash out because they feel under stress. It takes less to 'set them off' and less to make their moods swing. Angry moods do make accidents more likely for you and for your children, but they also might mean you clout them more often and more fiercely than you meant to. They can also mean that you won't be building up a warm, positive relationship with your child, but instead you'll end up being sharp with her. You may not be thinking of her needs and wants – you'll be too busy thinking about how yours aren't being fulfilled. You won't be giving her the cuddles and the love she needs; you won't be making her feel special. You may be constantly criticising and not making positive remarks and signals. You will not be helping her build her self esteem.

There is a difference between child abuse and not doing the best you know you are capable of as a parent. Of course there is. But remember that child abuse need only mean abusing the trust your child automatically and naturally places in you to meet her needs and act in her interests – and abusing the fact that in your relationship, you are the more powerful. Watch out for signs that you are out of control in the way you deal with your child and seek help. The last thing any of you want is for the problem to get out of hand.

DON'T KEEP THINGS TO YOURSELF

Don't be afraid to seek help, either. For a start, it is no reflection on you either as a parent or as a human being. All it shows is that you have enough insight to be able to see that you and your family need some advice or support. Remember, everyone gets help. Some people get it from their close circle, some get it from their partner – and some get it from those who aren't 'family' but whose role it still is to help: health visitors; social workers; family doctors; support groups and help lines. The other reason you shouldn't be afraid to seek help is because, whatever the horror stories you may hear, social service departments realise that the last thing they want to do is remove a child from her family. If you approach anyone about your child's welfare they will know you have her interests at heart and want to do your best for her. Unless it's an extreme case, you will remain in control. If it is an extreme case you must still take action for everyone's sake, but particularly for your child's. If your partner is the one who's abusing her, your loyalities may be split, you may fear that you'll lose all the security you have around you, but your first thoughts must be for your child.

TYPES OF STRESS

It's useful to look at the list of stress factors which the National Society for the Prevention of Cruelty to Children says are found most commonly in the families of abused children in England and Wales. They are:

- Marital problems – problems between the two partners. This is the most commonly found.

- Unemployment.

- The parent or parents being unable to respond to the developmental needs of the child. This means they don't understand, for example, that a 12 or 18-month-old won't be able to eat without making a mess. They'll expect her, and try to make her, do that.

- The parents are unable to deal with normal child behaviour. This means they won't be able to tolerate behaviour which is natural in children, such as their inquisitiveness, and their continual desire to try things and test things out.

- They will have unrealistic expectations of their child. They will be expecting too much from them. For instance they'll be expecting a very young child to understand the difference between right and wrong. They'll expect a child who is not skilled academically to do well in school, and not see that they have strengths in other areas.

- The family has financial debts.

Now these factors don't necessarily *cause* child abuse. After all, every couple with marriage difficulties doesn't abuse its children. They are factors noted in the families of children placed on local authorities' 'at risk' registers. And how common and every day those stresses on that list sound.

It's also interesting to look at the stresses involved in particular sorts of child abuse.

For *sexual abuse* the most common stress factors are marital problems, then unemployment. Next on the list is previous sexual abuse.

For *neglect* the most common stress factors are an inability to respond to the developmental needs of the child, then debts.

For *physical abuse* the most common stress factor is marital problems, followed by an inability to deal with normal child behaviour.

For *emotional abuse* the most common stress factor is marital problems followed by having unrealistic expectations of the child. The third biggest stress factor in this category is, poor self esteem on the part of the person abusing the child.

Again, these stress factors don't cause the abuse, but they do contribute to it. If you know you have marital problems, don't start to panic that you may be about to abuse your child, just be careful to consider your child's needs while you deal with your situation and try to work out some answers. Don't forget that sexual abuse and sadistic battering are planned in advance – you will never do these things as an automatic, uncontrolled response to feeling stressed.

EMOTIONAL ABUSE

Emotionally abused children are probably those who come to mind last when thinking about child abuse. It's easy to see bruises and battering, it's not so easy to see emotional scars. But many experts feel emotional abuse is actually more harmful in the long term. Continual verbal assaults, being called names, being undermined, constantly receiving negative criticism, not feeling loved or love being conditional on doing well at school or 'being good' – it's all very, very damaging. Just like other forms of abuse, it affects children from the mansion and children from the council block. Remember, a bruise can heal. But it's harder to heal inside when you've heard so many times, 'You're stupid.' 'You'll be the death of me.' 'You're ruining my life'.

A child may remind you of a husband or boyfriend who's no longer with you, of a grandparent or parent you didn't get along with. Her presence may simply remind you of what you see as your own inadequacies – why doesn't she behave well, why doesn't she look smarter, why won't she be the perfect child? Never take your own prejudices and your own anxieties out on your children. However well you feed them and clothe them and take care of their physical needs, they need emotional support too if they are to grow up healthy and happy.

If you are abusing your child in any form you are making your relationship with her difficult. You will find it much harder to carry out the true communication we've discussed, which will help her avoid hazards and dangers whether or not you're with her.

DON'T LASH OUT

If you find you're smacking and slapping a child, there can be problems. If you approve of punishing your child in this way, watch how and why you're doing it. Many parents hit young babies – even babies younger than a year old – and that's really no way to behave. Your baby is far too young for punishment. Never take out your frustrations by beating a child. After all, if you're unemployed it's not your child's fault – it may not be anyone's fault but it's certainly not hers – so don't take it out on her. If you're frustrated, scream into a cushion. Walk out of the room and count to ten. That's the joy of play-pens and cots and, more generally, keeping your home free of hazards – you can leave the room in safety, in moments like this. If you ever realise that the most dangerous thing in the room could be you, it means you must remove yourself, even briefly. That is a much safer thing to do if your child is left in a safe environment.

Every parent will have felt that frustration and stress. Some will succumb and hit their children, maybe harder than they intended. It really is a question of 'There but for the Grace of God go I.' But that doesn't make it right. People can cope with different amounts of stress, people have different amounts of difficulties and problems to cope with. So some can cope with an awful lot of stress because there are other, more positive things in their lives. Others will find a little bit of stress will make them act in an inappropriate way. What is important is for you to realise whereabouts on the scale of things you stand, and to take action from there. Recognise how you feel before you get out of control and lash out, either physically or verbally.

Remember, too, that your child will be the first to recognise stress in a family. And if there are times you are under great stress, don't ignore your children and hope they won't notice – explain that mummy is unhappy or mummy is tired.

Maybe you have a new baby who cries constantly. Don't take that out on your other children by turning on them and smacking them a lot. You may feel anger and resentment, but try to control it in the ways we've mentioned above. And try to be receptive to your baby, don't just see her as a crying bundle in the corner. Take note of when she's being good, too. If you're suffering from post natal depression, it may not be a good idea to mix with other mothers because they may make you feel more inadequate. Give yourself time for yourself, try to work your feelings through and seek help from the appropriate organisation (see addresses at the end of this book).

CHILDREN AND STRESS

At many times when you'll be feeling stress, your child will be feeling stress too. If she has to go into hospital you may be very worried, but don't forget she will be too. Stay with her as much as you can – overnights, too, if you're allowed. Take her own clothes and familiar things with her, and don't let her think it's a punishment. Try not to let your worry show, or your guilt if there's been an accident. If you have to go away, leave something with your child to look after for you, so she'll know you will be returning for her.

Remember, you may be very worried but she'll feel worried too, in an unknown world full of unfamiliar places without everything and everyone who makes her feel secure and happy. You must think of her in these circumstances.

If you are being beaten by your partner, your child can be hurt either by being caught in the crossfire, or by seeing her mother being bullied. Remember, it's not worth saving your marriage for your children's sake at any cost. It can do them more damage to live in a violent environment – and that means physically or verbally violent. Imagine the harm it does to a child for her to lie in bed listening to the constant fighting in the bedroom next door, hearing the two people she loves and depends on most, tearing each other apart.

DIVORCE AFFECTS CHILDREN TOO

If you are going through a divorce, you may well be devastated – it's the end of the life you've known. But it's the end of that life for your child too. So try to make it as easy for your children as you are able.

It's best if you and your partner deliver the news together, some time before one or other of you moves out. Show them it is a rational decision and that it is not the fault of the children. They will often believe that they are the cause of all the trouble around them, especially if it has been, at least in part, taken out on them. Explain that you both still love them, you just don't want to live with each other any more. They don't need to choose between you. They will want to know how the divorce will affect them personally – will they be sleeping in their own beds, in their own rooms? How often will they see the parent who's moving away? And tell them the new arrangement is forever. Most children of divorcees expect their parents to get back together again sooner or later. Don't take anything for granted – explain to them all you can, answer all their questions, ask their opinions, listen to what they're asking very carefully.

Your child may react in any number of ways. She may feel she's going to be abandoned, she may start to wet her bed, she may get depressed or angry or aggressive. An older girl might start looking at men much older than she is for affection. Don't get exasperated and think, 'This is all I need.' Understand that your children's world is crumbling around them. They'll be confused and scared as well as very unhappy. They need your support and your time and your reassurance. It's also important for the partner who's left to keep in regular contact with the children even if thir former partner remarries. A depressing statistic is that 40% of children stop having contact with one parent after a divorce.

BEREAVEMENT

If you've suffered a bereavement it will also be a time of great stress for you, but do think of your children, too. If you've lost a child don't just concentrate your thoughts on the one you've lost, you must think of the living as well. If you've lost a partner don't let your children feel they've lost both parents because one's gone forever and the other never smiles at them, never gives them any time. Explain to them what's happened, explain that you may not be able to give them all the attention they need for a while, if that's how you think you're going to react. On the other hand, explain to them if you think you're likely to explode suddenly with anger – anger that a person you love has been taken from you. If you don't manage to explain this beforehand, talk it through afterwards. You would be amazed at how often children feel they have caused life's ills. They'll feel responsible, they'll think you are angry at them.

SOME STRESS IS NATURAL

There *will* be stressful times during your child's development. The toddler tantrum stage may well be one. But try to understand the pressures your child feels, not just the affect her behaviour has on you. As the group Exploring Parenthood explains, your child will at last be able to move about freely and will want independence, but at the same time there are limits to her freedom which are important for her safety and for your convenience. Your child can get angry about being controlled in this way and she won't have the language to express herself. She'll want to do things her hands are not yet capable of doing which will be frustrating, she'll have to consider the wishes of others for the first time, she'll have to learn to control herself when it comes to potty training. Exploring Parenthood says that as well as recognising that your child is stressed, it's important that when you feel you must be firm you don't get fierce, if you get angry you don't get uncontrolled, when you are being strong you don't get aggressive.

There are many other stressful times in the life of a child but there are others more generally in the life of a family. There's moving home, illness, even holidays. There's the guilt many mothers feel about going to work and not being with their children all the time (even though by going out to work they'll be lessening other potential stresses such as unfulfilment, isolation and lack of money).

Social changes also make stress more likely. There has been a dramatic increase in the numbers of one parent families – and 81% of these are not single parents because of initial choice but because of death, separation or divorce. As well as the trauma of any of these, statistics show that one parent families are less likely to have many of the items that unquestionably make life easier and more comfortable such as a car, a washing machine, central heating and a telephone than a 'typical' family set up of two parents and two children. As we've said isolation may be a bigger problem – though not necessarily – and cashflow might be, too.

YOUR CHILDREN'S INTEREST

Adults can be very selfish when facing crises in their own lives and when they're feeling stressed. But if you don't consider your children's interests too, you'll simply have other stresses coming from them to add to the ones you already have. If you can't cope, then find someone who'll listen. We list at the end of this book some addresses of organisations who have volunteers who'll do just that. Listening is actually quite an art. It's one of the hardest things to do – to listen to what someone is saying and not try to control them or tell them what to do or what to think. We've already said that that's vital when you're listening to your children – when you're truly communicating with them – but it's also vital in relationships with other adults.

A lot of this book has been about accidents. And apart from ones caused by faulty goods, maybe you should consider how you're feeling and what's happening in your life if an accident occurs – either to you or to your children. They can be warning signs – you were too stressed to think that your toddler could reach that hot drink on the coffee table, you were too depressed to notice that your child had run on too far ahead.

But never forget, everybody gets stressed, everybody needs support, everybody needs help at some point in their lives. Don't feel guilty and hopeless if you lapse and your standards slip. Seek help, seek support. Work out what's happened and why it's happened.

Your children are individuals who need to be treated with the respect and care that all individuals deserve, but they are also more vulnerable and more dependent. They need you to guide them, to help them develop safely into adults. Take care of yourself – and take care of them.

Appendix A
SOME DANGEROUS
SUBSTANCES AND PLANTS

Some Dangerous Substances in the Home:
Ammonia
Bleach
Brake fluid
Caustic soda
Fertiliser
Lighter fuel
Methylated spirits
Oven cleaner
Paint
Paint stripper
Paint thinner
Paraffin
Petrol
Rat poison
Record cleaning fluid
Surgical spirit
Toilet cleaner
Varnish
Weed killer
White spirit
Window cleaning fluid

Some Medicines:
Aspirin
Calpol
Contraceptives
Sleeping pills
Thyroxine

Other brightly coloured pills/
tablets

Some Agents used in Solvent Abuse:
Aerosols
Anti-freeze
Butane gas
Car fire-extinguisher
Dry cleaning agents
Evo-stik
Other solvent-based adhesives
Hair lacquer
Lighter fluid
Nail varnish
Nail varnish remover
Paint thinner
Paint remover
Paints and lacquers
Petrol
Plaster remover
Shoe and metal polish
Solvent-based marker pens
Solvent-based sealants and dyes
Tippex thinning liquid

Some Poisonous Berries:
Black bryony
Black nightshade
Cherry laurel

Cotoneaster
Cuckoo pint
Daphne
Deadly nightshade
Firethorn
Hawthorn
Hemlock
Henbane
Herb paris
Holly
Honeysuckle
Lantana
Lily of the valley
Mistletoe
Philadelphus
Privet
Rowan
Solomon's Seal
Spindle tree
Virginia creeper
White bryony
Woody nightshade
Yew

Some Poisonous pods and seeds:
Broom
Columbine
Delphinium
False acacia
Foxglove
Horse chestnut
Laburnum
Lupins
Monkshood
Morning glory
Sweet pea
Thorn apple
Wisteria
Yew

Some Poisonous leaves:
Box
Dieffenbachia
Hellebore
Hypericum
Laurel
Lobelia
Poppy
Spurges
Tobacco

Appendix B
USEFUL ADDRESSES

British Standards Institution
Enquiry Service,
BSI, Linford Wood, Milton
Keynes MK14 6LE.
Tel: 0908 221166
This organisation can help you
discriminate between good, indifferent
and bad products.

Brook Advisory Centre
233 Tottenham Court Road,
London W1P 9AE.
Tel: 071-323 1522
This offers counselling for young
people.

Child Accident Prevention Trust
28 Portland Place,
London W1N 4DE.
Tel: 071-636 2545

Childline
Freepost 1111,
London N1 0BR.
Tel: 0800 1111
A free national telephone helpline for
children and teenagers in trouble or
danger. It is staffed by a team of
experienced male and female
counsellors, who will listen and
support any child with any problem.

Compassionate Friends
6 Denmark Street,
Bristol BS1 5DQ.
Tel: 0272 292778
This is a self-help group for bereaved
parents.

CRUSE
Cruse House, 126 Sheen Road,
Richmond, Surrey TW9 1UR.
Tel: 081-940 4818
This group offers help for the bereaved.

CRY-SIS
London WC1N 3XX.
Tel: 071-404 5011
Crying baby parents' support group.
Local contacts and groups throughout
the country.

Exploring Parenthood
41 North Road, London N7 9DP.
Tel: 071-607 9647
This group works with parents to
explore problems.

Families Anonymous (FA)
310 Finchley Road,
London NW3 7AG.
Tel: 071-431 3537
This organisation offers advice and
support for families and friends of
drug users.

Gingerbread
35 Wellington Street,
London WC2E 7BN.
Tel: 071-240 0953
One-parent families – support and
social meetings.

Health Education Authority
Hamilton House,
Mabledon Place,
London WC18 9TX.
Tel: 071-383 3833
This is particularly useful for
information about the care and
treatment of children or adults
infected with HIV or hepatitis B.

Home Start
2 Salisbury Road,
Leicester LE1 7QR.
Tel: 0533 554988
This group has several branches and
provides help in the home, support,
and friendship for families with young
children.

**Hyperactive Children's Support
Group (HACSG)**
59 Meadowside, Angmering,
Littlehampton,
West Sussex BN16 4BW.
Tel: 0903 725182
Dietary information and support for
parents of hyperactive children.

Incest Crisis Line
PO Box 32, Northolt,
Middlesex UB5 4JG.
Tel: 081-890 4732 (Shirley)
A telephone counselling service for
anyone involved in incest. It is run by
volunteers, both men and women
who have been victims of sexual
abuse.

Incest Help Line (Wales)
PO Box 350, Cardiff CF1 3XR.
Tel: 0222 733929 7.30–10.00p.m.
They can put you in touch with
support groups throughout Wales.

Kidscape
World Trade Centre,
Europe House,
London E1 9AA
Tel: 071-488 0488
This organisation works with children,
parents, teachers, police and youth
leaders to prevent all types of assault.

**Meet-A-Mum Association
(MAMA)**
58 Malden Avenue,
South Norwood,
London SE25 4HS.
Tel: 081-656 7318
Support and help with isolation and
loneliness.

**National Association for the
Welfare of Children in Hospital**
Argyle House,
29–31 Euston Road,
London NW1 2SD.
Tel: 071-833 2041
Advice and support for parents whose
children are in hospital.

NAYPCAS (National Association of Young People's Counselling and Advisory Services)
17–23 Albion Street,
Leicester LE1 6GD.
This offers listings of types of youth counselling available all over the country.

National Childbirth Trust
Alexandra House,
Oldham Terrace,
Acton, London W3 6NH
Tel: 081-992 8637
Antenatal classes, post-natal support and support with breastfeeding.

National Council for One-Parent Families
255 Kentish Town Road,
London NW5 2LX.
Tel: 071-267 1361
Information and support for one-parent families.

NSPCC (National Society for the Prevention of Cruelty to Children)
67 Saffron hill,
London EC1N 8RS.
Tel: 071-242 1626
This nationwide organisation deals with all aspects of child abuse. It provides a 24-hour service for children, parents and professional workers.

PARENTLINE OPUS (Organisation for Parents Under Stress)
Raysa House,
57 Hart Road,
Thundersley, Benfleet,
Essex SS7 3PD.
Tel: 0268 757077
Self-help and support group.

Parents Anonymous
6 Manor Gardens,
London N7 6LA.
Tel: 071-263 8918
This group offers counselling and meetings for parents who are tempted to abuse or have abused their children.

Re-Solv (The Society for the Prevention of Solvent and Volatile Substance Abuse)
St. Mary's Chambers,
19 Station Road,
Stone, Staffs ST15 8JP.
Tel: 0785 817885

Royal Society for the Prevention of Accidents (RoSPA)
Cannon House,
The Priory Queensway,
Birmingham B4 6BS.
Tel: 021-200 2461

RSSPCC (Royal Scottish Society for Prevention of Cruelty to Children)
Melville House,
41 Polworth Terrace,
Edinburgh EH11 1NU.
Tel: 031-337 8539
9.00a.m. – 5.00p.m. Mondays and Wednesdays
This covers all areas of Scotland.

SCODA (Standing Conference on Drug Abuse)
1–4 Hatton Place, Hatton Garden,
London EC1N 8ND.
Tel: 01-430 2341
This offers help if you suspect a member of your family or a friend has a problem with drug abuse.

Victim Support Scheme
17a Electric Lane,
London SW9 8LA.
Tel: 071-326 1084
A nationwide group of 300 schemes offering support and practical help to victims of violence and crime.

> **All addresses and telephone numbers are correct at time of publication. For further confirmation, visit or ring your local reference library**

TELEPHONE NUMBERS

Citizen's Advice Bureaux
these numbers are listed locally. Trained counsellors can give you details of local services available and help identify which is most relevant to your needs. Find your local branch in your telephone directory under 'Citizens'.

In support of Sexually Abused Children
081-202 3024 (Angela)
Monday to Friday
10.00 am–4.00 pm.

Irish Society for the Prevention of Cruelty to Children
Dublin 0001 761293/763051/760452

Mother of Abused Children
0965 31432

NCH (National Children's Home) Careline

Birmingham	021-440 5970
Cardiff	0222 29461
Glasgow	041-221 6722
Glenrothes	0592 759561
Leeds	0532 456456
London	081-514 1177
Luton	0582 422751
Maidstone	0622 56677
Manchester	061-236 9873
Norwich	0603 660679
Preston	0772 24006
Taunton	0823 333191

These numbers offer a confidential counselling service and are manned Monday to Friday 10.00a.m.–2.00p.m. and 6.00p.m.–9.00p.m.

Police Emergencies
Tel 999 anywhere
The police will respond 24 hours a day anywhere in the UK.

Rape Crisis Centres
The numbers of these are listed locally. They provide a confidential counselling service run by women, for women and girls who have been sexually assaulted or raped. There is a national network of centres.

Samaritans
The numbers of these are listed locally. They provide a 24-hour counselling service for anyone depressed, lonely or suicidal.

Social Services Departments
The numbers of these are listed locally. There are usually emergency numbers you can use out of office hours.

EMERGENCY FIRST AID

SOME SUGGESTIONS

WHEN TO CONSULT A DOCTOR ABOUT YOUR BABY

* *IF YOU THINK your baby is ill even without any obvious symptoms CONTACT YOUR DOCTOR*

* *IF YOUR BABY shows any of the following symptoms, especially if she has more than one YOUR DOCTOR would expect you to ask for advice*

ALWAYS URGENT
- a fit or convulsion, or turns blue or very pale
- quick difficult or grunting breathing
- exceptionally hard to wake or unusually drowsy or does not seem to know you

SOMETIMES SERIOUS
- croup or a hoarse cough with noisy breathing
- cannot breathe freely through her nose

- cries in an unusual way or for an unusually long time or you think your baby is in severe pain
- refuses feeds repeatedly, especially if unusually quiet
- vomits repeatedly
- frequent loose motions especially if watery (diarrhoea). Vomiting and diarrhoea together can lead to excessive loss of fluid from the body and this may need urgent treatment
- unusually hot or cold or floppy

Even if you have consulted a doctor, health visitor or nurse, IF BABY if not improving or is getting worse, TELL YOUR DOCTOR AGAIN THE SAME DAY.

WHAT TO DO:

In an emergency, don't panic. Try to keep calm. The child's life may depend on it, and calmness will help to comfort the child.

The really important things to check immediately are breathing, bleeding and consciousness.

1. Check breathing

If the child has stopped breathing, give mouth-to-mouth resuscitation (the kiss of life) immediately. Every second counts.

Mouth-to-mouth resuscitation

1. Quickly clear the child's mouth of any dirt, vomit, etc.

2. Bend the head back with one hand and push the jaw upwards with the other hand. This lifts the tongue off the back of the throat.

3. Squeeze the nostrils together, put your mouth completely over the child's mouth, and blow gently. See that the chest rises as you blow in.

4. Take your mouth away and let the air come out of the child's chest.

5. Repeat this about 15 times a minute. Keep on until the child starts to breathe again.

6. Then gently place the child in the 'recovery' position (see page 196).

Note: With a small baby, it may be easier to breathe into the mouth and nose at the same time.

If, after several breaths given mouth-to-mouth, the child is still very pale or a blue/grey colour, then the heart may have stopped. If you think the heart has stopped, give heart massage as well as mouth-to-mouth resuscitation.

Heart massage

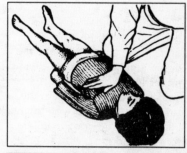

1. Lay the child on her back on the floor. Kneel by the child.

2. Press on the lower half of the child's breast bone. Use moderate pressure for a young child and even less for a baby. Press about once every second, quicker for a baby.

3. The child will not start breathing until after the heart has started beating. So after pressing 5 times, stop the heart massage and give a breath by mouth-to-mouth resuscitation.
   If there is another person with you, get them to do the breathing while you do the heart massage, stopping every 5 seconds to let the other person fill up the child's lungs.

4. Once the heart has started beating, keep on with mouth-to-mouth resuscitation until the breathing starts again.

5. Then gently place the child in the 'recovery' position (see page 196).

> *Note: It is best to learn how to give heart massage and mouth-to-mouth resuscitation properly. You can learn on a first aid course.*

2. Check bleeding
If there's severe bleeding, press firmly on the wound using a pad of clean cloth (if available) or your fingers. Keep pressing until the bleeding stops.

3. Check consciousness

It can be dangerous for an unconscious child to lie on her back because the throat can be blocked by the tongue or by vomit. So if the child is still breathing, but unconscious or very drowsy, it's important to place them in the 'recovery' position.

Recovery position

Turn the child half way over onto her front, with the underneath arm behind and the upper arm bent in front. Bend the upper leg so that it is at right angles to the trunk. Turn the face towards the ground with the neck back so that the tongue falls forward and the child can breathe.

If you think there may be broken bones or internal injuries, don't move the child unless you have to.

Never leave an unconscious child alone unless you have to. The child may stop breathing or choke.

4. If necessary dial 999

If you need help phone for an ambulance. Somebody else may be able to do this for you.

Broken bones

1. Don't move the child unless you have to. This is especially important if you think the child may have injured her spine or neck.

2. If the child has to be moved, be very gentle as you may cause further damage. If it's a leg that's broken, tie it gently but firmly to the uninjured leg before you move the child. Put some padding in between the legs.

If it's the arm that's injured and if it can be moved, put it in a sling or support. Be very gentle and comfort the child.

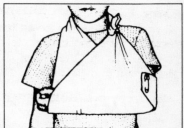

Always try to get expert help first before moving a child with a broken bone.

Don't give a child anything to drink after an accident if you think that an anaesthetic may be needed later.

Burns

1. Immediately put the burn under cold water, or run plenty of cold water over it, to reduce the heat in the skin. It's important to do this for at least 10 minutes.

2. Take off anything tight like a belt or jewellery. Burnt skin can swell up.

3. Then cover the burn with a clean, non-fluffy cloth like a clean cotton pillow case or linen tea towel. This cuts down the danger of infection.

4. If burnt clothes are stuck to the skin, don't try to take them off.

5. Then call an ambulance, or take the child to hospital. You should take a child to hospital for anything other than a very small burn.

Don't put butter, oil or ointment on a burn. It only has to be cleaned off again before treatment can be given.

Don't prick any blisters. You'll let germs in.

Choking

1. Don't waste time trying to pick the object out with your fingers unless it's easy to get hold of. Probably it will be too far back and too slippery.

2. Hold the baby upside down by the legs. Slap the baby's back smartly between the shoulder blades. If the object doesn't come out, do it again.

3. If after several tries this hasn't worked, as a last resort give the baby's tummy a short sharp squeeze. This should push the object out of the baby's windpipe.

Cuts

1. If there's severe bleeding, press firmly on the wound using a pad of clean cloth if available, or your fingers. Keep pressing until the bleeding stops. This may take 10 minutes or more. If it's a large wound, try to press the edges of the wound together.

2. Don't use a tourniquet or tie anything so tightly that it stops the circulation.

3. If possible, lay the child down and raise the injured limb. This helps to stop the bleeding. But don't do this if you think the limb is broken.

4. Cover the wound with a clean dressing.

5. Then call an ambulance or take the child to hospital.

6. If the wound is dirty, or the accident happened outside, ask your doctor about a tetanus injection.

Don't give a child anything to drink after an accident if you think that an anaesthetic may be needed later.

Poisoning
Pills and medicines

1. If you're not sure whether your child has swallowed something, spend a minute or two looking for the missing pills. Check they haven't rolled under a chair, for example. Don't spend too long looking around for it.

2. If you still think something has been swallowed, take your child straight away to your doctor or hospital - whichever is quickest.

3. If possible, take with you the container and a sample of whatever you think has been swallowed.

Don't give salt and water to make the child sick. Salt can be very dangerous in large amounts.

Household and garden chemicals - turps, petrol, paraffin, acids, caustics etc.

1. Gently give the child a glass of milk to drink. If there's no milk, give water instead. This dilutes the poison.

2. Then quickly take the child to hospital.

3. If possible, take with you the container and a sample of whatever you think has been swallowed.

Scalds

1. *Immediately* put the scald under cold water or run plenty of cold water over it to reduce the heat in the skin. It's important to do this for at least 10 minutes. Take off any clothes covering the scald so that the water can get to it.

2. Take off anything tight like a belt or jewellery. Scalded skin can swell up.

3. Next, cover the scald with a clean, non-fluffy cloth like a clean cotton pillowcase or linen tea towel. This cuts down the danger of infection.

4. Then call an ambulance, or take the child to hospital. You should take a child to hospital for anything other than a very small scald.

Don't put butter, oil or ointment on a scald. It only has to be cleaned off again before treatment can be given.

Don't prick any blisters. You'll let germs in.

Shock

1. If pale and unwell after an accident, make the child lie down.

2. If a lot of blood has been lost, keep the head down and raise the legs. This makes more blood go to the head. But don't do this if you suspect a head injury or broken leg.

3. Keep the child covered up and warm but not too hot.

Don't give a child anything to drink after an accident if you think that an anaesthetic may be needed later.

Suffocation

1. Quickly take away whatever is causing the suffocation.

2. If the child has stopped breathing, give mouth-to-mouth resuscitation.

A child should go to hospital after an accident if she:

- is or has been unconscious

- is vomiting or drowsy

- is bleeding from the ears

- has stopped breathing at some stage

- has lost a lot of blood

- may have internal injuries

- complains of severe pain anywhere

If you are worried or uncertain about a child's injuries, it's wisest to get a doctor's advice. You should go to the nearest hospital with an Accident and Emergency Department (Casualty), or to a local doctor, **whichever is quickest**. Not all hospitals have an Accident and Emergency Department, so it's worth checking where your nearest one is.

What to put in a first aid kit

1. Box of adhesive dressings (various sizes)
2. Box of sterile gauze dressings (various sizes) – for cuts
3. Small packet of paper tissues – to use as temporary sterile dressings.
4. 2 or 3 cotton bandages
5. 2 or 3 crepe bandages – for sprains
6. Triangular bandage, or clean old linen or cotton tea towel, or other cotton cloth – to use as a sling or as a large dressing for a burn or scald.
7. Small roll of cotton wool – for padding
8. Blunt-ended scissors

9. Safety pins and roll of adhesive tape – for fastening dressings and slings.
10. Small bar of soap – for washing dirty wounds
11. Antiseptic cream – for minor cuts etc.

> Always keep a first aid kit in the house. Keep another in the car. And always take a kit away on holiday with you.

USEFUL INFORMATION

Learning about first aid

If your child does have an accident, you'll be able to cope much better if you have learnt how to do first aid properly. The British Red Cross Society and the St. John Ambulance (or the St. Andrew's Ambulance Association in Scotland) run first aid and other courses, including emergency first aid courses. For information about courses in your area, contact:

Either your local Red Cross branch (address and phone number in your telephone directory under either 'British Red Cross Society' or 'Red Cross');

or your local St. John Ambulance branch, or if you live in Scotland, your local branch of the St. Andrew's Ambulance Association (address and phone number in your telephone directory).

The British Red Cross, St. John Ambulance and St. Andrew's Ambulance Association also run courses for young people in a wide variety of activities including survival, and accident and fire prevention.

The Royal Life Saving Society also run first aid courses. You can get details from:

The Royal Life Saving Society
Mountbatten House
Studley
Warwickshire B80 7NN.

Children can learn a lot about first aid and about safety by joining either the Scouts or Girl Guides. Your library or local youth office will be able to tell you where to find your local Scout or Guide unit.

Learning about water safety

Your children should learn to swim as early as possible. You can ask about lessons at your local swimming bath. It's also important for children to learn about water safety. You can write for information about this to the Royal Life Saving Society (address above) or to:

> The Royal Society for the Prevention of Accidents
> Cannon House
> The Priory Queensway
> Birmingham B4 6BS

Children should also learn rescue skills. Ask about lessons at your local swimming bath, or write for information to the Royal Life Savings Society (address on previous page).

Learning about road safety

Children aged three or over can learn about road safety by joining one of the 'Tufty' clubs organised by the Royal Society for the Prevention of Accidents. You can get details from the Road Safety Officer at your local authority. Look in the telephone directory for the local authority number, or write for information to the Royal Society for the Prevention of Accidents (address above).

If your child rides a bike, a Cycling Proficiency Test is a good idea. For details of courses run in your area, contact your Road Safety Officer (as above) or the Royal Society for the Prevention of Accidents (address above).

Home safety advice

There are a number of people who can give you helpful advice about how to make your home safer. Many local authorities have Home Safety Officers, usually working in the Environmental Health Department. The Environmental Health Officer may also be able to help, and so can your Health Visitor.

If you would like more information about water, road or home safety, the Royal Society for the Prevention of Accidents (address above) has many useful publications and can answer your queries.

INFANT CARE GUIDANCE

Feeding:

Breast feeding is the natural and the best way to feed your baby. Coughs, colds and tummy upsets are less frequent in breast fed babies because breast milk helps them to resist and recover from infection. The early months of breast feeding are the most valuable. You and your baby will succeed best if you are quiet and undisturbed when feeding.

If you cannot breast feed or if you decide at some time to change to bottle feeding, keep the bottles and teats sterilised. Use a recommended baby milk up to the age of 6 months. Following the instructions for making up the feeds accurately and carefully. If your bottle-fed baby appears hungry, the amount given at each feed and/or the number of feeds can be increased, but do not strengthen the mixture by adding extra milk powder. Never leave a baby sucking at her bottle on his own. Very few babies need solid foods before the age of 3 months, but most want a mixed diet as well as milk feeds by the age of 6 months. Consult your health visitor or doctor about feeding and vitamin supplements.

Babies aged over 1 month are sometimes thirsty and want a drink of water (without sugar), which has been boiled once only and cooled. This is especially important if they are feverish or have a cold, a chest infection, diarrhoea or vomiting. Illness is hardly ever caused by teething.

Crying:

All healthy babies cry from time to time; some babies cry much more than others; and some babies cry regularly at a certain time of day. If crying continues and is not due to the usual causes - hunger, thirst, discomfort, wet or soiled nappies, tiredness, loneliness or being too hot or cold - and gentle rocking of the pram or cot or cuddling does not settle the baby, then see your doctor or health visitor.

Sleeping Position:

Select a cot with a firm, well-fitting mattress; a baby does not need a pillow. Traditionally, new born babies were put on their side to sleep with the lower elbow a little in front of the body, and put down on the opposite side after the next feed; this is still good practice. A rolled nappy placed by the back will prevent the baby rolling onto her back. Some babies like to sleep on their tummy, with the face turned to one side. As the baby grows the position in which she settles happily is probably the best.

Temperature:

Keep your young baby's room at an even temperature of about 65°F (19°C) both day and night. Newborn babies need to be well wrapped until about one month old after which they are better at keeping themselves warm. Protect your baby including her head from draughts and use the pram hood in chill winds. In cold weather a baby can lose heat quickly even in her cot or pram. To check whether your baby is warm enough put your hand beneath the covers to feel her body. If the room is too warm or the baby overclothed, a baby can get too hot; she will feel hot or sweaty to touch and may be thirsty. Fresh air is good for a healthy baby, but not when she has a cold, or in foggy or cold weather. In hot weather keep the pram hood down and shade your sleeping baby from direct sunlight with a sun canopy.

INDEX

ACKNOWLEDGEMENTS

Many people have helped us with advice and information. We are particularly grateful to:

Ann Baumber, Educational Psychologist;
The Child Accident Prevention Trust;
Shirley Clark;
Maria Dabrowska of *PARENTLINE OPUS*;
Pat Gray of *CRY-SIS*;
Prue Harrison, for her considerable editorial help.
Jane Horrex;
Meg Lindsay;
Ros Meek of *The Health Visitors' Association*;
The National Society for the Prevention of Cruelty to Children;
Sarah Neville;
Dr. Jim Thomson, Department of Psychology, University of Strathclyde;
Noreen Wetton, Health Education Unit, University of Southampton;
Mike Wilkins, Senior Social Worker specialising in child sexual abuse, team member of *Exploring Parenthood*;
Angela Willans;
Dr. Richard Woolfson, Child Psychologist;
Bernadette Wren, Clinical Psychologist, The Great Ormond Street Hospital for Sick Children and

We have used *Play it Safe*, a booklet produced by The Health Education Authority, *Keep Your Baby Safe* and *Keep Them Safe* produced by The Child Accident Prevention Trust, *Drug Misuse – a Basic Briefing* and *Drugs – What Every Parent Should Know* produced by the Institute for the Study of Drug Dependence, *Alcohol and Health* produced by the Medical Council on Alcoholism, *Keeping Safe* by Trefor Williams, Noreen Wetton and Alysoun Moon of the Health Education Unit, University of Southampton, information from Re-Solv, *How to Help Your Child Manage Without You* and *Is Your Child Safe In Your Car?* from Practical Parenting Magazine.